W9-BNY-964

1. The Little Bishop

The LITTLE BISHOP

Episodes in the Life of St. John Neumann, C.SS.R.

by

Paschal Turbet, C.SS.R.

ST. PAUL EDITIONS

IMPRIMI POTEST
Very Rev. Joseph L. Kerins, C.SS.R.
Provincial, Baltimore Province
Redemptorists
March 1, 1977

NIHIL OBSTAT
Msgr. Carroll E. Satterfield, S.T.D.
Censor Librorum

IMPRIMATUR
✠ Most Rev. William D. Borders, D.D.
Archbishop of Baltimore

March 14, 1977

In conformity to the Decree of Pope Urban VIII, the author unreservedly submits all statements herein to the judgments **of the Holy See** and the decisions of the Sacred Congregation of Rites.

Library of Congress Cataloging in Publication Data

Turbet, Paschal.
The little bishop.

1. Neumann, John Nepomucene, Bp., 1811-1860–
I. Title.
PZ4.T9285Li [PS3570.U625] 813'.5'4 77-6232

Printed in U.S.A. by the Daughters of St. Paul
50 St. Paul's Ave., Boston, Ma. 02130

The Daughters of St. Paul are an international religious congregation serving the Church with the communications media.

CONTENTS

Preface ... 9
Introduction ... 11

Episode

1. John and Louisa ... 13
2. A Poor Report Card ... 19
3. Doctor, Lawyer, Priest ... 25
4. Seminary Days ... 32
5. The Waves Grew Higher ... 40
6. Ordained a Priest ... 44
7. Frontier Pastor ... 50
8. Moccasins in the Ravine ... 57
9. His Brother Wenzel ... 61
10. Redemptorist Novice ... 65
11. The Storm on the Patapsco ... 70
12. Mother Theresa, S.S.N.D. ... 76
13. Sick Call to Elkridge Landing ... 84
14. Expelled from School ... 87
15. The Pectoral Cross ... 94
16. Margaret's Marble Statue ... 103
17. Moyamensing Prison ... 107
18. The Sisters of St. Francis ... 111
19. Back Home in Bohemia ... 122
20. The Forty Hours ... 128
21. With His Boots On ... 136
22. John Neumann in Glory ... 143

Memorable Dates in the Life of John Neumann ... 147

Preface

In this the canonization year of St. John Neumann, C.SS.R., we welcome this latest addition to the published works on the life of our American Saint.

Brother Paschal Turbet, C.SS.R., in *The Little Bishop* has selected a score of events from the lifetime of John Neumann and from them has created a mosaic of the career, the trials, the labors, and the glory of this heroic servant of God. He was small in stature, simple in lifestyle, a human being with whom any of us would feel at ease. But he grew to heroic size and shows that is possible for all of us.

Through the pages of *The Little Bishop* we follow John Neumann from his youth in Bohemia, through his seminary days, his journey across the ocean to America, his apostolic labors first as a Diocesan Priest and later as a Redemptorist Missionary. We read of John Neumann's life and ministry as the Chief Pastor of the Philadelphia Diocese, his untimely death, and the holiness of his life that has, in our day, enrolled him among the saints of the Church.

We all share in the life and glory of St. John Neumann. In his life we can all find inspiration and strength. He is, for many reasons, a part of the "American way of life."

Our Holy Father, Pope Paul, has presented John Neumann as model not only for Americans but for the faithful everywhere, for he has stated: "An adoptive son of the United States is shown to the Universal Church as an example of holiness. As a layman, as a religious, as a priest, as a bishop, he gives every rank of the Church a model to imitate."

May the publication of *The Little Bishop* bring a greater knowledge of the life of St. John Neumann to all who read its pages.

Joseph L. Kerins, C.SS.R.
Redemptorist Provincial Superior

March 19, 1977
Solemnity of St. Joseph

Introduction

There are currently several biographies of St. John Nepomucene Neumann, C.SS.R., Fourth Bishop of Philadelphia. This presentation is in no sense a biography. Rather, it is a series of episodes and incidents in the life of Neumann which I have woven into the short story form, the better to show John Neumann for what he actually was—a lovable, down-to-earth man of God.

The basic facts of the episodes and incidents are for the most part taken from the definitive life of "Bishop John Neumann, C.SS.R." by Rev. Michael Curley, C.SS.R., and from a biography now out of print by the Bishop's nephew, Rev. John Berger, C.SS.R. In his Foreword to Curley's Life, Cardinal A. G. Cicognani, then Apostolic Delegate to the United States, has written: "With vivid lines Father Curley has drawn for us a picture that is most faithful (to facts) and attractive...the soul of John Neumann defies complete description. The author has given us the facts and has analyzed them to some extent and challenges us to go even deeper if we would discover the treasures of Neumann's character."

This is what I have endeavored to do, to delve deeper into the treasure of John Neumann's character, so that he will be better known and appreciated.

The Author

EPISODE 1

John and Louisa

The Neumann family loved little Louisa, Louisa with the flaxen hair, red cheeks and dancing blue eyes. She was a favorite with John, who liked to take her along on his jaunts through the woods. Mrs. Neumann said they would spoil the child with all the attention they gave her.

Louisa on her part was quick to take advantage, to get her own way around the house. Seeing John so interested in his school books, she took it into her head that she wanted to go to school with her brother and gave him no rest until he had asked permission from the schoolmaster.

They left home that morning hand in hand, John with a bag of books over his shoulder, Louisa in her best Sunday dress, her hair combed back in two short braids tied with red ribbons.

"Promise, Louisa," John turned to his sister, "promise you'll behave in school today." Louisa promised, "crossed her heart." She really meant it at the time.

Other children came out of their front doors and joined the trek to the parochial school, chattering and laughing along the narrow streets of the small Bohemian town.

At the open door of the classroom John waited with Louisa. Behind a big desk in front of the classroom sat Mr. Karolik, the schoolmaster, staring sternly across a row of books at the children.

"Ack, so! This must be little Louisa. Good." At the sound of his booming voice, Louisa suppressed a giggle. "She will sit with you, John. Your partner can take the empty desk at the back."

The morning sun shone through the open windows on four rows of double desks. John took his place in the first seat by the window, settled Louisa on the bench and arranged his books.

Class opened with prayer. Thirty heads were bowed, thirty pair of hands folded on the edge of the desks. Louisa too bowed her head and folded her hands. She behaved nicely during religion period, bowing her head each time she heard the name of Jesus and of God. John was proud of his little sister.

Though German was spoken at the Neumann house, the complexities of German grammar bored Louisa. Tired of sitting on the hard bench, she slid to her feet and stood in the aisle. John quickly sat her back on the bench and settled her with a pencil and paper on which to draw pictures. Louisa liked to draw pictures.

There was a written test that morning in arithmetic. The master began to copy long columns of numbers on the blackboard which the pupils were to copy and total up. Now arithmetic was John's weak subject, and he could not afford any distractions from Louisa. Resting his left elbow on the desk, he set his head sideways in the palm of his hand so as to shut off Louisa. Soon he was busy battling with the columns of figures. On the desk behind, a hand slid slowly forward, gave a quick tug at one of Louisa's braids.

Portrait of John Neumann, age 10

"Our Mother daily heard
mass to which she
took one of us."
c Neumann Center, Philadelphia, Pa

Louisa gave a loud giggle. Turning from the board and taking the pencil from behind his ear, the master waggled it in warning to Louisa.

John was embarrassed, mortified that his sister had vexed the schoolmaster. When the correct answers were read out he had three wrong—three out of five, a failure. The test papers were collected and placed on the master's desk. Never again would he take Louisa to school.

"Now, boys, I must go over to the Rectory to see Father Schmidt. I'll be back in twenty minutes." The master assigned them a page of sums from their arithmetics. "John Neumann," he called out. Oh no, thought John, it's about Louisa. "John, you be monitor while I'm gone. Write down the name of any boy who talks or misbehaves." John Neumann took his post by the desk of the master. The boys settled in silence to work at their sums.

Louisa, now alone and without the moral support of her brother who had his back to her, knelt up on the bench to take a good look at the boys. No one seemed to pay any attention to her. She set her elbows on the desk behind, the desk of the boy who had pulled her braid. She liked this fat boy with all the freckles. She started to giggle. Freckles, with pencil in his finger tips, waggled it at Louisa, even as the master had done. Quick as thought Louisa waggled her pencil right back at Freckles. That did it. Freckles exploded with glee. Every head snapped to attention. Louisa was smiling at them all, Louisa with red ribbons, and blue eyes dancing with mischief. Louisa Neumann at that minute was Queen of the Day.

But Louisa, true to form, overplayed her part. She waggled her pencil at the whole class from one side to the other. Bedlam broke loose, the boys laughed and guffawed and shouted, clapped their hands and continued to clap. In the noise and confusion John did not know what to do. To write down all the names would do no good. Yet the master had left him in charge and would expect him to keep order. Slowly he went over to Louisa, took her by the arm and marched her across to the master's desk and stood her on the platform. The clapping stopped, the laughter subsided. The boys had great respect for John Neumann.

But Louisa still had her audience and she knew it. Instead of showing repentance, Louisa again started to giggle. In one quick swoop, John swung his little sister into the master's chair, hidden from view behind the row of books on the desk. The curtain had come down on Louisa's little act.

When the schoolmaster returned he found the class in perfect order, everyone working and on John's list only one name, that of Louisa Neumann, the little girl fast asleep in his chair behind the barricade of books.

He looked from Louisa to John, turned to the class and slowly smiled, "Good work, John, good work." He placed his hand on John's shoulder. "Some day when you grow big, you will become a teacher. No?"

EPISODE 2

A Poor Report Card

When he was twelve years old, John Neumann in the company of twenty other boys from Prachatitz left home to attend high school in the Gymnasium of Budweis then under the direction of the Piarist Fathers. Studies came easy to young John Neumann mainly because of the night class tutoring of Father Schmidt. But at the end of his third year a crisis developed.

That morning a group of students, most of them home-town boys, left the city of Budweis and took to the open road homeward bound for vacation. It had been a long hard year.

The religion teacher had been boringly dry, and their Latin professor, an easy-going old man often under the influence of liquor, had to be dismissed in mid-term. His successor, full of zeal and determined to make up for lost time, loaded the boys with so much work that many just could not keep up and became discouraged.

But all this was over now, at least for the next two months and the boys were carefree and happy. Traveling in groups was such fun. They stopped to rest on the roadside grass and opened their bags for an encouraging snack.

"Whoopee!" shouted a fat boy taking out his report card, tearing it into small pieces and flinging the pieces into the air.

"You should not have done that, Jakob," chided Neumann.

"Listen to who is talking," piped out a tall slim boy. "Neumann, you didn't do too well yourself." His report card went up in small pieces. More report cards went up and fell into the dusty road. Half the boys had failed and were quitting the Gymnasium for good.

When the march resumed Neumann slowed his pace and dropped behind the others. It was true what Slim had said, only too true. John's report card marks were poor, slightly above failure. He was disgusted.

"Come on, Neumann," a friend yelled back. "Catch up. I have an extra Budweiser for you." He waved a bottle of beer over his head.

Neumann shook his head. He did not drink. He wanted to be alone to think this thing out. A failure almost! He was disgusted with himself, with the new professor, with his books.

Adalbert Schmidt dropped out of the group to walk along with Neumann. Tall for fifteen years and quick in studies, Adalbert had from the first taken a liking to the gentle, serious boy from Prachatitz. John and Adalbert became fast friends.

"What's wrong with you, John?" asked Adalbert. John said nothing. "I know you are thinking of quitting. Tell me, John. I'm your best friend."

"Adalbert, I'm disgusted, ashamed of myself. Is it worthwhile going on like this?"

"Don't," pleaded Adalbert, "don't quit. You have the brains. And if you quit, you are a coward. The good Lord would not like it one bit."

Adalbert had touched the right spot. John Neumann did not want to displease the good Lord. But what would his father say when he saw that miserly report card? What would he do?

Hoofbeats were heard behind. A horse and carriage approached, causing a cloud of dust on the road. There standing in the seat was Father Meyer who taught fourth-year Latin at the Gymnasium. He was well liked by the whole school. The boys clapped and cheered.

"On my way to Prachatitz," he shouted. "See some of you there." He snapped the whip and went galloping down the dusty road.

Though John had been home from school more than a week, he told no one his trouble. In a burst of confidence he finally told his sister Veronica. Veronica knew her brother well and extracted from him the cause. Their mother must be told. Mrs. Neumann was surprised at first and shocked. Could this be the end of her fond dream of one day seeing her John at the Altar as a holy priest of God? With a little persuading John agreed not to give up his studies but to go back the next term and make up for lost time.

One day when supper was finished and grace had been said, Mr. Philip Neumann and his wife lingered over a second cup of tea. The girls were in the kitchen washing the dishes. John and little Wenzel waited patiently for their parents before leaving the table.

"Come to think of it, John," said Mr. Neumann, "where is your report card? Isn't it time you showed it to me?"

This was the moment he dreaded. "It's up in my room, Father."

"Go get it," his mother said. Where her husband was concerned, she knew it was useless to postpone.

John brought back the report card, handed it to his father and remained standing. Mr. Neumann read down the list of subjects, stroked his chin, took out his spectacles and wiped them clean on the end of the table cloth. Mrs. Neumann lit the lamp.

"John." There was sadness in Mr. Neumann's voice. "It appears that you are no longer interested in your studies. So you will stay home from school and learn a trade."

John hung his head. Mrs. Neumann gave a gasp:

"Father, I am sorry. May I go up to my room?" As he passed her chair, Mrs. Neumann clasped his arm. His four sisters stood silently in the doorway.

"And John...," John turned on the stairway. "...You will report to me tomorrow morning at eight o'clock to learn the knitting trade."

Next morning and each morning for weeks after, John started work in his father's downstairs knitting mill. Though disappointed at his father's decision and discouraged, John showed no resentment but only worked the harder at his tasks. Only his mother and Veronica knew how much he wanted to continue his studies.

Sunday Mass was over. The crowd of worshipers dispersed to their homes. The Neumanns stood outside their big house on Linzer Street chatting with the neighbors. When Mr. Neumann excused himself and went back to the garden to have a look at his apple trees, John followed his father down the walk. Veronica at a nod from her mother followed John into the garden.

"Father," said John, "I have something I want to ask you."

"Speak out, son. You are doing very well in the mill. You learn quickly. I'm proud of you."

"That is not what I mean, Father," John pursued. "I'd like—I would like to go back to school next November."

"But, John, your marks." His words were gentle. "You can understand that I will allow no son of mine to be wasting his time and my money in a distant city."

"Mother thinks I should go back to school and have another chance."

"Yes, Father," put in Veronica. "We feel deeply on this."

"You too, Veronica. Outnumbered I see. Still no reason for me to change my decision."

"We have been thinking, Father. How about another examination for John? Father Meyer from the Gymnasium is now in town staying with the Smutneys. Why couldn't he give John another test? That way you would know for sure."

Since the feastday of St. Wenceslaus was a national holiday, the Neumann knitting mill was closed. The family was in the garden, John up in the apple tree dropping the ripe apples into his father's hands, while Catherine and Veronica bedded and covered the rose bushes against the coming winter. Mrs. Neumann sat in a chair sewing.

"Father, Father!" Little Wenzel ran down the garden walk. "There is a man at the gate asking for you."

"Bring him in here, boy."

Father Meyer in riding togs and cap strode into the garden.

"Glad to meet you, Mr. Neumann. I'm on my way back to Budweis. The horse and carriage are waiting at the gate."

John dropped from the apple tree onto the grass beside Father Meyer, who put his hand on John's shoulder. "Mr. Neumann, I am happy to report to you that your son has done remarkably well in the test. Take my advice, sir, and send that boy back to school."

"Mother!" shouted Mr. Neumann. "Come here. Did you hear what Father Meyer said? John is to go back to the Gymnasium. Bring out the special brandy, and we will all drink a toast to Father Meyer, to John and to good King Wenceslaus."

Veronica followed her mother into the kitchen to help bring out the wine glasses.

"But, son, tell me why you did not study while in Budweis?"

"I just could not, Father. My roommate was always entertaining friends in our room."

"That settles it. Next year you must have a room all to yourself."

Everyone drank his toast to good St. Wenceslaus, to Professor Meyer and to John's success in his future studies.

EPISODE 3

Doctor, Lawyer, Priest

John Neumann had graduated with honors that morning from the Institute of Philosophy in Budweis. Back in Prachatitz the Neumanns were anxiously waiting his homecoming. Wenzel stationed himself at the gates of the town to watch the road. Mrs. Neumann and his sisters were preparing a special supper, *veprove se zelim,* as she called it.

"He's coming, John's coming." Wenzel ran up the stairs and burst into the kitchen. "Mother, Dad, John is coming down the road."

"Where is he now?" Mr. Neumann asked folding his newspapers.

"Near Berger's farm." Wenzel was out of breath.

"That would be a half mile out of town," Mr. Neumann remarked. "Mother, he should be here in ten minutes."

Mrs. Neumann swung into action.

"Quickly, Catherine, bring the soup to a boil and start dropping in the dumplings. You, Veronica, stir the sauerkraut and whip up the potatoes nice and fluffy." When she opened the oven door to have a look, the aroma of roast pork filled the kitchen. "Dad, come with me where we'll be out of the way."

Wenzel followed his parents into the dining room to help set the table for supper.

"Mother, is John going to be a priest?" Wenzel asked.

"Wenzel dear, you must not ask such questions. That is for John himself to decide. Off with you now to meet John. And take Louisa and Joan along. Take turns carrying his bag."

"Agnes," said Mr. Neumann to his wife when the children had left. "I don't know but the boy is right. It is about time someone in the house knew just what his intentions are."

Supper was finished. It was so good to have John home again.

When grace had been said, Mr. Neumann pushed out from the table to allow the girls to clear off the dishes. John rolled his napkin into the napkin ring, continuing to fill his parents in on all that happened the past six months. In the kitchen there was a clatter of dishes and a happy chatter. Mrs. Neumann rose and tied on an apron to help the girls in the kitchen.

"Don't leave, Mother," said Mr. Neumann. "The girls can take care of things. Come into the parlor where we can talk—you, John and I."

He took the deep mohair chair by the fireplace and filled his meerschaum pipe.

"How old are you now, John?" He lighted the tobacco with a flame from the fireplace.

"Twenty years, Dad, this past March 28th."

"And you liked your studies?"

"Yes, Dad, very much." He took the diploma and report card from a side table and handed them to his father. "I think you will be pleased with the marks."

Mr. Neumann scanned the diploma written in Latin and poured over John's grades.

"Good, son, this is very good. The question now is: what are you going to do with all this knowledge? Have you in the course of all this studying made up your mind as to what you want to do with your life?" His vocation? John had been considering that for the past six years. While at the Gymnasium he conceived a strong desire for the priesthood, which was later dissipated by his ardent love of the German poets. While studying chemistry and physics he had toyed with the idea of continuing on to medicine. The Jesuits later entered under his scrutiny, but he knew so little about the Society of Jesus. The Cistercians preoccupied his desires for a while. Right now he was much inclined to the diocesan priesthood.

"Now see here, son. In all these years you have come to no decision. If you are to continue on in your studies, we must know soon. In two months the universities will be reopening."

His father was pressing too closely. How could John explain to his father the insurmountable obstacles to becoming a diocesan priest?

"How about the priesthood?"

John hesitated.

"A lawyer?" his father persisted.

John was not interested in law.

"I know, John. Become a doctor. It's a noble profession. You like people. As a doctor you could help them very much."

Mr. Neumann was on familiar ground. John's face brightened.

"You would make a good doctor. And I would be only too happy to help you through. As to expenses we could manage it somehow."

"Dad, I think I will." His voice was decisive. "I would like to go to study medicine."

The grandfather clock in the hallway struck seven – seven slow sad strokes. Mrs. Neumann left the room to hide her tears. The chatter in the kitchen had ceased.

The family went to bed early that night. The house was in darkness except for the lamp still burning in the upstairs room. John sat at his table, his head buried in his hands. It had been an exhausting day; the graduation that morning, the fifteen mile hike home, and lastly the encounter in the parlor with his father.

Had he made a mistake in choosing to become a doctor? Was there any hope at all of getting into the seminary? He heard the stairs creak and then a gentle tap on the door. His mother was standing outside holding a lighted candle.

"Come in, Mother. What keeps you up so late?"

Mrs. Neumann sat on the edge of the bed, with a look in her eye that John had never seen. The glow from the candle perhaps.

"Mother, I'm glad you came. I'm worried."

"I knew you would be. That's why I came."

"Do you or dad have friends who are influential? Outside of Prachatitz I mean. Say in Budweis or Prague?"

"Why do you ask, John?"

"Well, to get into the Seminary of Budweis you must have an influential friend as sponsor."

"I knew it all along," said Mrs. Neumann with exaltation in her voice. "So you do want to be a priest?"

"Yes, Mother, more than anything in this world."

"But why, why did you tell your father that you wanted to be a doctor?"

Veronica broke the hush with a loud clap. Everyone clapped, everyone laughed. The girls gathered around their father to see the Bishop's letter. Mrs. Neumann sat down and cried into her apron. Wenzel hugged his big brother. John pressed the boy's head to his shoulder. When supper was resumed no one noticed that the soup was cold. The whole family was too thrilled, none more than John Nepomucene Neumann. God, through the voice of the bishop, had called him to the holy priesthood.

EPISODE 4

Seminary Days

John Neumann entered the Seminary of Budweis in November, 1831. To his great joy Adalbert Schmidt was enrolled the same day. Friends since the early days at the Gymnasium, the two formed an ideal friendship—John, calm and deliberate; Adalbert, quick and self-assured.

The director of the Seminary, Father John Koerner, in the course of his lectures on Scripture one day gave the class such a stirring presentation of St. Paul's missionary journeys that the whole seminary talked about it for days. Adalbert later confided to John that he intended to become a missionary and go to America. John encouraged Adalbert but only a month later, after mature consideration, did he tell Adalbert that he too was determined to go on the American missions.

Their friendship took on an added depth. Study and prayer were their one preoccupation. Every minute of their time was directed to the one goal—to prepare themselves to become good missionaries. Though professors marveled and classmates wondered, John and Adalbert kept their plans a deep secret. A mutual friend, John Savel, was admitted in on the secret and agreed that he too had been thinking of the American missions. Now there were three.

Visions missionary
vocation to save faith
of Immigrant to America

In each other's rooms the three friends would meet in spare time to plan, to discuss and to pray for their future. Accounts from missionary magazines were read, reread and talked over. The labors of the famous Father Baraga among the American Indians, the work of the Redemptorists in the big cities, the appeals of the Bishop of Philadelphia for priests to come to his diocese fired their zeal to still greater heights.

Father Baraga advised those who would come to America to acquire languages, especially French and English. The three friends began to study French, to read French and on their walks into the countryside to speak French. But English? You could learn English only from someone who spoke English. No one in Budweis spoke English.

Neumann had an idea. Courses in English were taught at the University of Prague, not far from the Seminary of Prague. Now the Bishop of Budweis had the privilege of sending each year two of his seminarians to the seminary in Prague to finish their courses. Neumann's request to be sent there was so compelling that the aged bishop could not resist. John Neumann would go to the Prague Seminary and Anton Laad would be his companion. Neumann was disconsolate. For the first time in years he and Adalbert would be separated.

In the spring of 1835 a handsome red coach drawn by two black horses drove up to the front entrance of the Prague Seminary. The seminarians with cassocks flapping in the wind were promenading about the grounds. A footman climbed down from the driver's seat and opened the coach door. Two gentlemen in tall silk hats stepped out and, addressing no one in particular, loudly asked to see the Father Director. They were escorted into the parlor. "Why, yes," said the director, a stout, gray-haired priest, "I have just the man you want." He stepped into the corridor and asked a passerby to bring John Neumann. Neumann, his hair disheveled by the wind, entered, giving a long look at the two gentlemen, and cast his eyes down.

"I give you the Rev. Mr. Neumann," said the director.

The gentlemen had a proposition which they were confident Mr. Neumann would find most advantageous. A position in the Royal Embassy was open for a young man well versed in languages, especially French and English. The work was not strenuous and the salary considerable with every chance for advancement. Would Mr. Neumann care to consider the proposition?

John Neumann raised his eyes and gave the two gentlemen one of his penetrating looks.

"No, gentlemen," he said in a low voice. "I am sorry to disappoint you. Thank you all the same."

The gentlemen looked at each other in disbelief, and then turned to the director.

"But why, John?" The director was embarrassed. "You would still do priestly work on weekends." Neumann continued staring at the floor carpet. "And you must realize by now that the Budweis diocese already has too many priests."

"Father," said Neumann, "I learned those languages for the American missions. I intend going to the United States."

Vocally disgusted, the two gentlemen snatched their tall silk hats and flounced out of the room. The director gave Neumann a look of pity and went back to his room. Neumann walked down the corridor to the chapel. No matter what others thought, the good Lord in the Blessed Sacrament would understand.

His last year at the Seminary of Prague was coming to an end. One more month and John Neumann would be back in Budweis for the one great day of his life, the day of ordination as a priest of God. Then off to the States, he and Adalbert together. In May a disturbing rumor reached Prague that Adalbert Schmidt intended to join the Cistercians. Neumann was stunned, deeply hurt. That John Savel had dropped out he could understand, but Adalbert—never. To change his mind like this and not even a hint to his best friend! Neumann refused to believe the rumor.

One night on returning to his room from chapel, he found an envelope on his door. Adalbert's handwriting! He lit the candle and tore open the letter.

Seminary of Budweis

"Dear John,

Word has reached us here of how you refused the offer from the Royal Embassy. Good work, John old boy." Relieved and gladdened Neumann read on. "Now for the big news. As you know, Father Dichtl of the Cathedral is my father confessor. Well I finally told him of our plans. You would not believe the interest he took. He knows a certain Canon Räss in Strassbourg who has contacts with a number of American bishops. He has even promised to take up a collection among the priests of the diocese to cover our traveling expenses. John, old boy, we have not a worry in the world. Just pray that we be more worthy of the call."

Adalbert Schmidt

But there was cause for worry, more worry than John or Adalbert could imagine. Word was sent out in June that Bishop Rudžička had taken seriously ill and that ordination had to be postponed. Sorely disappointed, Neumann left Prague and took the stagecoach home. Weeks of waiting followed. When he did recover, Bishop Rudžička showed no hurry to ordain the class. Neumann's patience was sorely tried. Souls in America were being lost for lack of priests, and here he was home in Budweis powerless to help them.

At long last, word was sent out that ordinations had been postponed indefinitely. The news was shattering. Too many priests in Budweis and souls in the States crying for priests. Neumann had waited seven months. He would wait no longer. He would set out for America even without ordination and be ordained there.

Breaking the news to his family was a painful ordeal to him and to the family. His four sisters sat with tears rolling down their cheeks, and except for the brave intervention of his pious mother, his father would have refused consent. As for Adalbert, John was worried. He had not seen or heard from him in weeks.

The clock in the Budweis Cathedral boomed out the hour, frightening off the pigeons and dislodging a shower of snow. Neumann looked up at the clock. Two o'clock. Time enough for a visit to the Blessed Sacrament before taking the long road home. It had been a strenuous day for Neumann procuring his passport, persuading the bishop to allow him to leave the diocese. And then he saw Adalbert Schmidt coming down the rectory stairs.

"Adalbert Schmidt. Am I glad to see you! How have you been anyway?"

Adalbert was all right, he guessed.

John took the passport from his inside pocket and passed it to Adalbert, who after a cursory glance gave it back.

"Anything wrong?" Neumann was perplexed.

"Not here, John. Let's go where we can talk." Adalbert led the way along a shoveled path to a spot behind the Cathedral.

"Something is terribly wrong. What is it, Adalbert?" Fear tightened the muscles of his throat.

"I don't like to tell you this, John, but I am not going to America with you." Adalbert turned away, unable to face the hurt in John's big eyes. "The whole business is too risky. No ordination. And as yet no written acceptance from an American bishop. Besides Father Dichtl's collection barely netted enough travel money for one man."

A drift of swirling snow enveloped the two friends behind the Cathedral.

"I understand your position, Adalbert." Neumann's voice showed no resentment. "And I respect your reasons. You are only doing the prudent thing. But as for me, I must go on. I must and I will get to America. Adalbert, will you pray for me?"

With his hand on John Neumann's shoulder and tears in his eyes, Adalbert promised that every morning when he stood at the altar he would ask the good Lord to protect his friend, wherever he was.

One cold morning while it was still dark, John Neumann with two traveling bags stole out the back door, passed under the city gates and took the long road to Budweis, arriving in time for the last Mass in the Cathedral. Long after the congregation had left, Neumann was still on his knees begging his God for the courage to go on despite the homesickness gnawing his heart. When he came out, he found Adalbert waiting for him to keep him company as far as Einsiedln.

The stagecoach went crunching along through the Black Forest through snowbanks as high as the stage windows. Sitting side by side on the cold bench, neither John nor Adalbert had much to say. At a time like this, words seemed empty.

The stage arrived in Einsiedln two hours later. With his long arms Adalbert reached John's bags from on top, gave them to his friend, grasped his hand and turned quickly away.

John Neumann was alone now, all alone to face an unknown world, dejected and homesick but determined with God's help to reach the missions in the United States.

EPISODE 5

The Waves Grew Higher

The story of John Neumann's journey to America is a saga of incredible determination. With only forty dollars in his pocket and what donations he could beg from friends in Budweis he started on a trip that took him halfway across Europe. Always hungry and weak, despite loneliness and dejection, he pushed on and on from town to town, from city to city, from one Holy Communion to the next.

He arrived in Le Havre, the port city of France, on April 17, 1836, for his first view of the ocean. The limitless expanse of tossing water thrilled his drooping spirits. The sailing vessels crowding the piers sent his hopes sailing high. After putting a decent meal in his stomach, he began to look at the ships, to question the ships' masters. The *Europa*, a big three-master bound for New York, seemed the most likely, its captain the most friendly. Captain Drummond agreed after some bargaining to take the young man aboard at the reduced rate of eighty francs, all John had left except for some small change. Neumann was bound for America at last.

When the ship was thirty days out, a storm loomed on the horizon. The sea grew rough and rain began to fall. In order to ride out the storm in safety, Captain Drummond decided to change course and sail with the wind. Sails were lowered and securely tied; the drift anchors were tossed overboard to reduce speed and the storm-sail was unfurled to the wind. All passengers were ordered below deck.

"Who is that up forward?" a sailor shouted over the rising wind. "He'll get washed overboard."

A solitary figure lingered in the prow of the ship, heedless of the coming storm.

"Get below, you fool!" Captain Drummond shouted through his megaphone. The man in the prow did not hear him.

"Oh, that's Neumann," sneered a burly Bavarian, "the little Bohemian who wants to be a priest. He thinks he can pray back the storm."

When the hatches had been battered down, the sailors dispersed. Some went below. Captain Drummond and a group climbed into the pilot house and bolted themselves in, leaving Neumann alone on deck. Danger was never a deterrent to John Neumann.

He wanted to be alone, away from the crowded hold, alone to think things out, to assess his prospects of the future, if the Bishop of New York should refuse to accept him into the diocese.

An eerie darkness enveloped the ship. Winds shrilled through the shrouds and rain lashed the deck. Heedless of cold and rain, Neumann felt the cold hand of despondency grasping his hopes. If priests were so badly needed, why had the Bishop of Vincennes ignored his applications? And the Bishop of New York? Was his answer lost in the mail? Why did God let this happen to him?

The ship was handling beautifully, riding the waves like a plow through a field of furrows. Slowly she crept up the side of a gigantic wave, balanced herself for a moment on the crest, then slid down in the twilight of a seething trough. The sea rose to within a few feet of the deck.

Neumann was heedless of the rising dangers. His thoughts raced on. Had his applications been ignored because he was not yet ordained? Ordination. That was the hardest blow of all. For four years he had prepared for ordination, had prayed for ordination only to be told at the last moment that there would be no ordinations that year. Ordination had been postponed indefinitely. Obstacle after obstacle. Was God trying to tell him that ordination was not for him?

"No, God. Dearest God, no!" he cried into the roar of the storm.

Again the ship crept up on a crested wave, balanced herself and plunged into the seething trough. The sea was now inches from the deck.

Neumann's soul reached out to his God. The one desire of his life was to be His priest, to work for the souls He had saved. Why had God hidden His Face?

At the next plunge into the trough, the sea poured over the gunwales sweeping the deck clear. Neumann's feet were pulled from under him, but his hands had held on to the ropes. He was still on deck, awakened from his thoughts and alert to his own personal danger. The ship sailed on through the waves. Suddenly he felt his hands loosened from the stay ropes over his head, and as if by some invisible hand pushed and shunted three feet to one side. Came a sharp report overhead, followed by a tremendous crash that threw him to the deck stunned and trembling. The forward mast had snapped in two and had fallen to the deck on the very spot where he had been standing. Death had missed him by three feet. Divine Providence had saved his life. God did, after all—God did want him a priest.

When the wind died down and the sea subsided, the captain and crew picked their way forward through the tangle of ropes to inspect the damage. There beside the fallen mast knelt the figure of the lonely seminarian. Peace and calm had returned to the soul of John Neumann.

EPISODE 6

Ordained a Priest

The *Europa* sailed into New York harbor after six weeks at sea. It was cold and raining the day John Neumann walked off the gangplank onto American soil. But nothing could dampen the ardor of his spirit, his happiness of being in the United States after all those trials, now in the land of his dreams where he hoped to be ordained and work for neglected souls.

And it was Corpus Christi, the great feast of the Blessed Sacrament. He must by all means find a Catholic Church where he could thank his God for all He had done for him, for having saved his life at sea. All that afternoon through rain and drizzle he tramped the streets of New York in search of a church with a cross on top. Night was closing in. His coat was soaking wet, and water oozed in through the holes in his shoes. Weak and hungry he had to give up the search. The good Lord would understand.

On a side street he found a German inn, where with the last change in his pocket he paid for a warm supper and a bed for the night. Next morning the kindly innkeeper gave him a free breakfast and sent him on his way to a nearby Catholic Church. There in the presence of the Blessed Sacrament John Neumann

"What emotions were
mine when I set foot
on American soil."

poured out his heart. Afterwards the pastor, Father Schneller, heard his confession and advised him to see the bishop's vicar-general, Father John Raffeiner, at St. Nicholas Church on East 2nd Street.

Father Raffeiner at first glance took the caller to be a beggar but changed his mind and took Neumann into the parlor and gave him a chair. Suspicion gave way to curiosity as he listened to the astonishing story of Neumann. But this was fantastic—his claim to be a seminarian seeking to be ordained for the New York diocese. Neumann went bravely on. He wanted to know whether Bishop Dubois had received his application from Canon Räss of Strassbourg.

"You know Canon Räss?" Father asked. Neumann nodded. "Well, that application was received, and Bishop Dubois had sent a letter of acceptance to Canon Räss three weeks ago."

Neumann gave a sigh and sat back in his chair. He had been accepted, Father Raffeiner was saying, and he would be ordained.

"And," pursued Father Raffeiner, "you have that letter of acceptance?"

"Letter of acceptance?" repeated Neumann. "Father, I have been on the high seas these past six weeks."

"But why, why?" Father Raffeiner was angry. "Why did you not wait for the bishop's answer before coming here to us?"

"The truth of the matter is, Father, I did wait in Paris as long as I could, till my money ran so low that it was either return home with small hope of getting to the missions or take a ship for New York. Trusting in the help of God, I came on."

A tear glistened in Father Raffeiner's eye. This astonishing young man had left home and country, and had risked everything to become an American missionary.

"Well, John," he said softly, "you do have credentials, letters of recommendation?"

Yes, John Neumann had them in the pages of his Bible, one from the chancellor of the Budweis diocese, another from the Bishop of Linz and his seminary records. He opened the cord of his duffle bag, took out his books and his few belongings and from his Bible handed the papers to Father Raffeiner. Slowly, word by word, Father Raffeiner read the documents and then read them again. Neumann's lips moved in silent prayer.

"Mr. Neumann," Father Raffeiner's voice was jubilant. "These are excellent, extraordinary. You are the answer to our prayer. Bishop Dubois is in sad need of a priest for the missions of the Buffalo sector."

Neumann grasped his hand in joy. All his troubles were over.

"But wait a bit," Father Raffeiner said, "I don't see any dimissorial letters."

"Dimissorial letters..." Neumann whispered. This was a point that had disturbed his conscience. He had none.

"Yes, the letters of release from your former bishop. You do have them?"

Neumann confessed he had none. The old bishop was too sick at the time, but the chancellor had promised to send them later.

"Well, let's not worry about that right now. Bishop Dubois can and will, I'm sure, dispense from them. So let's lose no time. You and I must hurry down to tell him the good news."

Neumann started to repack his things into the duffle bag.

His first Mass prayer:
"Dearest God,
Give Me Holiness
SANCTUS
SANCTUS
© Neumann Center, Philadelphia, Pa.

"Never mind the bag, John. You will be my guest here until further orders. But first you and I must go downtown to buy some decent clothes. We do want to make a good impression on the bishop, you know."

Two weeks later on the morning of June 25, 1836, at a quiet ceremony in old St. Patrick's Cathedral on Mott Street, Bishop John Dubois imposed hands on the head of young John Neumann making him a priest of God. Neumann's heart overflowed with happiness. His only regret was that his mother and family were not present. The next day, Sunday, before a crowded congregation in St. Nicholas Church, Father John Neumann stood at the altar and offered up to God his first holy Mass. He was now a priest forever and ready to begin his life's work for the salvation of souls.

EPISODE 7

Frontier Pastor

Soon after Ordination, Father Neumann was sent by Bishop Dubois to the Buffalo sector of New York State to assist Father Alexander Pax who was overworked and broken in health. It was agreed between them that Father Pax would give full time to Buffalo and that Father Neumann being young and strong would try to cover the surrounding territory some thirty miles square with central headquarters at the crossroads of Williamsville.

It had snowed all that day, and night was closing in. In the deepening shadows of the forest road a weary traveler trudged through the falling flakes. At a bend in the road he paused to straighten the pack on his back and gave a soft sigh of relief on seeing a log cabin ahead with curling smoke coming up from the chimney. He brushed the snow from his coat, made the clearing and knocked on the door. After a wait, the door was cautiously opened.

"Pardon me, lady," he said. "I've lost my way. May I come in a while?" Then he added, "I'm Father John Neumann, the new pastor of Williamsville."

"A priest of God, did you say?" The woman threw open the door. "Glory be to God! A priest of

Bishop Neumann
A
Frontier
Priest

God knocking at my door, this blessed night. Come in, Father! Come in, come in out of the cold. And welcome it is to our poor cabin." She stepped aside and bowed the priest in.

"God bless this house and all who live in it," he said and stepped in.

A poor cabin indeed; rough log walls lighted by the blaze of an open fireplace, a dirt floor and a rough table with children's faces gathered around the glow of a lantern. The good woman could not thank the priest enough for honoring them on such a terrible night.

"But God forgive me. Here I am thinking of myself and the poor priest half frozen. Tommy," she turned to the children, "run out to the woodshed and bring in your father, and a big armful of wood." She looked at the pack strapped to Father Neumann's shoulders. He pulled off his mittens to find his fingers too numb to undo the buckles. "Here, Father, let me undo it for you." She opened the buckles and set the pack on the table. "My, Father, what a heavy load you are carrying!"

"My Mass kit, the chalice, the Missal and vestments," he said.

"It is ages, Father," she said sadly, "ages since we last heard holy Mass."

The cabin door opened, a cold gust blew in, followed by the master of the house, a tall, burly man with gentle blue eyes that looked directly at the little priest. With a glance to his wife, he set the wood by the hearth and stood before the priest.

"Welcome this blessed night, Father, to my hearth and home." He wiped the palm of his hand on the seat of his pants and extended it to Father Neumann.

"Cald mille, falte, soggarth aroon." Father Neumann grasped his hand with a warm squeeze.

"Just an old Gaelic welcome to the priest of God," he added in explanation.

"But wait a bit, Father Neumann. We haven't yet been properly introduced. I'm Michael O'Neill, a woodcutter at the lumber camp near Niagara Falls." He turned to his wife. "My wife Mary." Mary O'Neill dropped a curtsy. "And my five children. Come here, children, and meet the good Father."

Five bashful children lined up before the priest who sat with his back to the warmth of the fire, smiling happily at their fresh faces.

"This is Nora, my oldest." A girl of twelve stepped forward and dropped a curtsy just as her mother had done.

"And this is Tommy. Pardon, your Reverence, Thomas."

"Let it be Tommy." Father Neumann gave Tommy a wink. Tommy beamed shyly.

"And Mary." Mary dropped a curtsy, a slow, solemn curtsy.

"And John." John stepped smartly forward, wiped his hand on his pants, just like his father, and grasped the priest's hand.

The introductions came to a close when Kathy, a moppet of three, attempted to curtsy and toppled over in tears. Father Neumann picked up the child, sat her on his knee and wiped away the tears. That did it. The children crowded around Father Neumann in a burst of instant friendship, a friendship sealed by a bag of hard candy from Father Neumann's pocket.

"Mary dear," said Mike O'Neill, "are we forgetting? Father must be starved. How about a bite to eat for all of us?"

Father Neumann had been fasting since early morning and was now hungry and weak—very weak. Lunch was set on the big table: thick slices of hearth-baked bread, a loaf of cheese, and cups of piping hot tea. Father Neumann ate slowly, sipping the hot tea and answering Mike's questions about the chapel at Williamsville. Grace was said, and while he and Mike sat by the fireside, Mary and the children cleared off the table.

"You'll stay the night with us, of course," said Mike.

Father Neumann was startled. "No, Mike, I cannot. Please, Mike, don't misunderstand me. I would like nothing better than to spend this night with you and your family. But I must be in Cayuga Creek by morning." Mike turned to his wife, astounded. "Souls will be waiting there, Mike, waiting for Mass and the Sacraments. I must be off again—tonight."

Mary O'Neill stood by her husband. "But, Father, you just can't make it in this storm. Cayuga Creek is ten miles northwest of us. Why you'd, you'd..." tears choked her words.

"I must, Mrs. O'Neill. I must make it by morning. And with God's help, I will. He has not failed me yet."

Such tenacity of purpose, such reliance on God's Providence. How do you convince such a man?

"Excuse us a minute, please, Father." She nudged Mike and took him to the back bedroom.

While their parents consulted, the children jostled around their little priest pleading with him not to go away, but to stay with them until morning. With a sad smile, Father Neumann promised to come back soon to tell them all about Jesus.

"Father Neumann!" There was a finality in Mike's voice. "To get to Cayuga Creek tonight is

Bishop Neumann
at home with
the poor.
© Neumann Center,
Philadelphia, Pa.

impossible. But I have a plan. Jake Werner, our neighbor down the road, has a horse and snow pung. You stay with us tonight and tomorrow early we can all drive to Mass in Jake's snow pung. Tommy can trek down to Jake's on his snow shoes to tell Jake of the plans."

Father Neumann gave a quiet smile. How good God was! He let him get lost in the storm only to lead him to these lost sheep of the fold. And now He was arranging for the Mass tomorrow morning. Father Neumann nodded to Mike. Yes, he would stay. The children clapped and jumped with joy. Mike and Mary clasped his hands.

At Father Neumann's suggestion they all knelt down for the rosary before going to bed. And such a rosary, with the logs crackling in the fireplace, the wind whistling outside around the corner of the cabin, and the peace of God breathing on the humble household.

A cot was set up for the priest near the fireplace, and the family retired for the night—the children up the ladder to the loft, Mike and Mary O'Neill to the back bedroom. Father Neumann finished the Divine Office by the light of the dying fire and had settled under the blankets when soft whispering came to his ears.

"A holy man, Mary, a holy man."

"A saint, I tell you Mike, a saint of God. Every Hail Mary he said I thought I was in heaven!"

The sublimity of simple faith, thought Father Neumann.

"O God, have mercy on Your poor, unworthy priest!" Tears coursed down his cheeks into the pillow.

EPISODE 8

Moccasins in the Ravine

It was late afternoon. In the deepening dusk of the ravine Father John Neumann trudged wearily home. He would soon be safely home in his little two-room rectory in North Bush. A sudden dizziness came over him. Perhaps if he rested and untied the pack from his back.... He fainted and fell forward into a bramble bush at the side of the path and lay there for some time.

When consciousness returned, he rolled out of the brambles and propped his back against a tree trunk. He tried to think. How had he gotten here? He remembered he had said Holy Mass that morning in Cayuga Creek. He wiped the blood from his hands and face. Somehow his senses seemed unusually alert to the chirping of the birds in the trees, to the evening fragrance of the wood flowers, to the pulsing silence of the forest.

But what was that? At the front end of the ravine he had seen—he was sure of it—he had seen a movement in the underbrush. He sat motionless and waited. The bushes parted and he saw something or someone dart behind a tree. He was being followed. Again the bushes parted, and he saw it plainly, a brown body and a feathered head. Probably a Huron Indian on the prowl. But why? To rob him or worse?

His memory flashed back to the missionary accounts of the famous Father Baraga among the Indians of northern Michigan. Indians, he wrote, respect fearlessness, are won over by courage. "Dear Lord," he murmured, "give me courage for the sake of this poor child of the forest."

Looking up again to the ledge, he saw the Indian standing in full view, brandishing a knife in his hand. For a full three minutes each kept his eyes fastened on the other, the Huron with his knife on the ledge, Father Neumann sitting against the tree, neither moving an eyelash. The Huron was dressed in leather breeches and except for a collar of beads around his neck was bare to the waist.

The Huron grew impatient. Though the little white man was apparently unarmed, he did not deign to rise, much less to run away. In one smooth movement, the Indian thrust the knife into its sheath and leaped off the ledge, landing on the path as gracefully as a wild cat. Step by step, he drew nearer to the white man. Still no sign of fear. He halted and swung his arm over his head in a come-on motion. A second Indian leaped from the other ledge, and two others appeared at the rear end of the ravine and began closing in on him. Still no sign of fear or fright from the little white man. The leader stopped and gave the signal to the other three to halt.

"Good evening, my friends," said Father Neumann in a soft, gentle voice extending the hand of friendship. The leader was puzzled. Was this some kind of a trap? Father Neumann then made a surprising move. With his extended hand he made the sign of the cross over them pronouncing the blessing

Indians care for and carry the fatigued missionary home

in Latin. The leader stepped back and grunted. He knew that sign, the same sign he had learned from his Huron grandfather, who had learned it from the early Jesuit missionaries. This little man was a blackrobe. He got down on one knee, made the cross over himself, went up to Father Neumann and clasped his hand. The other three gathered around their new friend.

Seeing Father Neumann too weak to rise, they unrolled a deerskin blanket, placed him on it and holding the four corners over their shoulders carried their little blackrobe to his little rectory in North Bush.

Father Neumann, seated on a chair in his kitchen and living room, saw for the first time the shriveled arms and bloated stomachs of his new friends. The poor men were starved and, no doubt, prowling around for food. He took out a big wheel of cheese, set it on the table and sliced four big wedges and gave one to each Indian with a big slice of bread. His face glowed with happiness to watch them devour the food. Though he offered them the whole wheel of cheese, they would agree to accept only one half of it. They all kissed his hand, and with much smiling and bowing they left their little blackrobe for the silent trails of the forest.

"Thank You, dear God," whispered Father Neumann. "Thank You for helping me out. But do, Lord, somehow, in Your own way, do bring my poor friends to the knowledge of Your loving Goodness."

EPISODE 9

His Brother Wenzel

Father Neumann had been over three years on the Niagara frontier, three lonesome soul-searing years. Repeated letters to Europe pleading for priests brought no response. But he did receive a letter from his brother Wenzel, who notified him he was coming to America to help him in his missionary work.

Father Neumann was overjoyed. He had not heard from his family since he left home. All their letters to him had miscarried. Wenzel was like a breath of fresh air to his drooping spirits. Under Wenzel's loving care, the log cabin rectory became a decent home, a vegetable garden flourished in the rear and Father Neumann, relieved of his teaching in the two rural schools, traveled in widening circles in search of his scattered flock.

One afternoon in late summer John and Wenzel were in the Williamsville chapel, constructing a new altar for Mass.

"John," said Wenzel pulling out his pocket watch, "it's now after four o'clock. Hadn't we better start for home? You know how the horses panic in the darkened forest trails." John continued sawing as if he had not heard his brother. "What's bothering you, John? I just don't understand you anymore." John set the saw down and looked straight at Wenzel. "I have something to tell you, Wenzel, something very important. Not now, but on our way home. If you round up the horses, I'll take the tools back to Mr. Weyrick."

Dusk sifted down through the tree-tops. A damp fragrance rose from the earth. John and Wenzel rode their horses side by side along the forest trail. Neither spoke a word. Wenzel waited for the "important" news. The lonesome call of a bobwhite cut through the silence.

"Well, John, what is it? This big secret of yours?" The only boys in a family of four sisters, John and Wenzel grew up in a special friendship. And secrets were no part of their friendship.

"Now Wenzel, you are not being fair," John reined his horse to a stop. "You know I never keep anything from you unless I have to."

"But I just don't know you anymore, John. You are a changed person since that sickness. And now all these extra visits to Buffalo to see Father Pax."

John's words were slow and deliberate. "Wenzel, as I lay sick in bed those three months, I did some hard thinking—thinking about my future." Wenzel straightened in the saddle. "I have finally decided with the full consent of my confessor to become a religious, a Redemptorist. I am writing to Father Prost in Baltimore, asking for admission.

The lonesome bobwhite gave out a triple call.

"That means," Wenzel's voice was hoarse, "that means that you will be leaving me and North Bush."

"Please, Wenzel, please. I was hoping you'd come with me. I must go. I must live a life of greater perfection. I must get closer to my God."

Suddenly the two horses whinnied in fright and reared up on their hind legs. A deer had crossed the trail and went rustling off through the underbrush. John quickly reined in his horse and brought him down. Wenzel and horse dashed off in a wild gallop and disappeared in the darkened trail.

Wenzel was angry, angry like John had never seen before. And he had good reason. If only he had been told before, this would not have happened. Yet it would have been unwise to burden Wenzel with doubts when he himself was not sure. This decision had to be made between his own conscience and his confessor. Poor Wenzel! O God, why must I always hurt those I love the most? John took out his rosary and rode home through the deepening shadows.

Two weeks later, John was returning home from a three day sortie across the border in Canada, tired and saddle-sore but consoled that the dying trapper had made his peace with God. Birds twittered evening prayer in the boughs overhead. Nearing North Bush a sadness settled on his mind, a sadness for his brother Wenzel. For two weeks Wenzel hardly spoke. Never once had he referred to John's decision to leave North Bush. What was going on in his mind? If he would only break this impasse.

At the next bend in the road the log cabin rectory came into view. A thick column of white smoke rose from the chimney, and from the open door came singing—Wenzel was singing. John stabled Jupiter for the night and stood in the doorway amazed to see the table neatly set for two and Wenzel busy at the cook stove.

"Come in, John, come in!" Wenzel was his old cheerful self. "We are having a feast tonight, *veprove se zelim*, just like mother used to make back home in Bohemia." John remained in the doorway.

"But, Wenzel, I don't understand all this extravagance and waste."

"Simple enough," explained Wenzel. "While you were in Canada, I rode into Buffalo to do some shopping."

"So I see," John was not fooled. He knew of old Wenzel's indirect approach. Could it be...?

"And John, while in Buffalo, I had a long talk with Father Pax." Wenzel was now deadly serious. "Remember saying that you had to get closer to God? I too want to be a Redemptorist, a Redemptorist brother."

John took Wenzel by the arms and put his head on his shoulder. "Thanks be to God" was all he could say.

"Come, come now, I do believe my reverend brother has tears in his eyes."

"Oh Wenzel," murmured John. "I'm so happy, happy that we are to be real brothers again, brothers in the Congregation of the Most Holy Redeemer."

EPISODE 10

Redemptorist Novice

During his four lonely years on the Niagara frontier, Father Neumann came to the reluctant conclusion that he should join a religious community. Though Bishop Hughes tried to dissuade him and the people pleaded, he felt he had to leave. A higher life was calling, and he had no choice but to go. In November, 1840, he was welcomed into the Redemptorist Community by the Fathers of St. Philomena's in Pittsburgh.

What he saw in his first few weeks convinced him that he had made the right choice. The sincere holiness of the community, their work among the people, the mutual respect and help, left little to be desired. Here he could let his soul unfold and get really close to his God.

Anyone wishing to join a religious community must, according to Church law, pass through a year of novitiate to test his vocation. But the Redemptorist Fathers in those early days had no house of novitiate and Father Neumann was their first American novice. It was decided that he should remain with the Pittsburgh community and Father Chackert would be his novice master.

Father Chackert wrote out an order of the day for his novice to follow. Each morning he gave him a spiritual conference, when he was not away on the missions, advising and counseling him on matters of the soul. Neumann on his part drank in his every word, and like a child with his own father revealed to him the depths of his heart. Father Chackert secretly admired the mature holiness of the young priest.

One evening after supper, when the Fathers were at recreation, conversation for some reason began to lag and stop. Father Rector could not understand it until he noticed that Father Neumann, usually cheerful, was completely silent.

"Father Neumann," he said, "aren't you feeling well tonight?"

Although Neumann replied that he was all right, Father Chackert was not convinced.

"Tell us, Father," he said to his novice, "just what is wrong?"

"It's only a foolish dream I had last night. I haven't been able to shake it all day."

"Oh so, a dream?" said the novice master rising to the occasion. "Tell the Fathers all about this foolish dream of yours."

"Must I, Father Master?" Neumann pleaded.

"When your novice master asks," his tone was severe, "an obedient novice does not refuse." This was a reprimand. Father Neumann dropped to his knees, as a good novice should.

"Go ahead, please. Humiliation is good for the soul." Father Chackert as novice master had the right to humiliate his novice.

"Well, in this dream I was sitting at my desk when a bishop came into the room all dressed in cope and mitre. He seemed to know me. He sat down beside my desk. He said—he said—" Neumann could not go on. At an urging look from the novice master, he finished in a rush of words. "He said he wanted to send my name to Rome for a vacant bishopric."

A pregnant silence gripped the Fathers. Everyone there knew that a Redemptorist priest takes a vow to refuse all bishoprics and honors unless ordered by the Holy Father to accept. No one spoke. Father Rector wiped his spectacles. The novice master broke the silence. "There must be more. Go on," he said.

"I froze with fright. I begged the bishop not to. He persisted, and then he took off his pectoral cross and was trying to place it over my shoulders when I awoke."

The novice master to all appearances was unimpressed. "You kneel there and openly talk of your bishopric. You have no right even to dream of such a thing."

Father Neumann stared at him with his big dark eyes. The novice master was twisting his words completely. He did not believe him. An angry blotch burst on his forehead for a moment. Then Neumann regained his calm and hung his head.

The Fathers were enjoying the little drama. Aspiring to be a bishop? Father John Neumann? Ridiculous! The novice master was putting on a good act.

"Wait," continued the novice master. "Wait until you have finished your novitiate. Then all your proud fancies will disappear. Pray that you may persevere as a good simple Redemptorist."

"God grant it," was Father Neumann's only reply. No complaint, no resentment, no explanation.

First to join
Redemptorist Fathers
in America.
c Neumann Center, Philadelphia, Pa.

A smile crinkled the corners of the novice master's mouth when he noticed the intent look of Brother Wenzel.

"Brother Wenzel," he said, "take a good look at that big brother of yours. Just like a naughty school boy." Turning to Father Neumann he said, almost with admiration, "Father, get up and take your seat with the rest of us."

Father Neumann rose from his knees and took his seat, relieved at last of the weight of his dreaded dream.

EPISODE 11

The Storm on the Patapsco

Father Neumann's first assignment was to the busy parish of St. James. He threw himself into the work, hearing confessions, preaching, instructing converts and teaching religion to the children. Outside of Baltimore were settlements of Catholics who had no priests, in many places no chapels. Claiming this difficult work as his own because of his experience on the Niagara frontier, he made regular trips to Overlea, Frederick, Cumberland, wherever a priest was needed.

It had come to his attention that an isolated colony of Bohemian farmers on Curtis Bay were without the Sacraments. The fastest way to reach Curtis Bay was by rowboat. He went by rowboat, regularly each month.

One summer afternoon he left St. James Rectory with the Mass kit on his back, and taking a companion he walked across the city to the piers at Boston Street and hired his rowboat. The rowboat pushed through the waters of upper Baltimore Harbor. Father Neumann in black frock coat and black hat sat on the stern seat reading the breviary. The lazy lapping of the waves against the sides and the warm sun on his back seemed to promise a smooth crossing.

Bishop
Neumann
AS
A
Redemptorist
Missionary
© Neumann Center, Philadelphia, Pa.

"Let me know when you are tired, Joe," he said looking up from the breviary. "I'll take a turn at the oars."

"Not yet, Father," Joe Soler bent his back to the oars.

Father Neumann liked young Joe Soler. It was Joe who first told him of the sorry plight of the farmers on Curtis Bay. Each month on the trip to Curtis Bay, Joe would come along as his oarsman and altarboy.

Reaching the opposite shore of the river, Joe followed the shoreline. Woods and beaches passed calmly by.

"All right, Joe. Time for a rest." Father Neumann closed his breviary.

They were half way to Fort McHenry. When Joe had shipped the oars and they had changed seats, Father Neumann braced his feet against the sides and gave one powerful pull that sent the boat leaping through the water.

"You learn fast, Father." Joe was proud of the fact that he had taught Father Neumann to row.

"Look out," Joe cried in alarm. "Quick–strong on the left."

Father Neumann gave two quick strokes with the left oar just in time to avoid a head-on collision with a submerged rock. But the blade of the oar hit the rock and snapped out of the oarlock into the water and was retrieved by Joe in the stern seat. In order to avoid more rocks, Father Neumann took the boat out into deeper water. It was good to breathe in the piney fragrance that drifted out to the boat.

Rounding the point, he rested on the oars to take in the view of Fort McHenry. As they looked on, two soldiers came out of the Fort, marched across the parade grounds and though it was mid-afternoon proceeded to lower the American flag. But why was the other soldier raising a pennant on the beach?

"That's a storm warning for small craft," explained Joe.

Downstream about three miles where the Patapsco meets the Chesapeake Bay, storm clouds blackened the sky and the river ran white with tossing waves. They scanned the distance across to their landing beach. Could they make it in time?

"It's too risky, Father." Joe was frightened.

"Don't be afraid, Joe. We'll make it before the storm breaks. People will be there waiting for us."

He took off his hat and coat and with one mighty stroke lifted the bow out of the water, leaving a swirling wake behind the stern. In five minutes they were well off from the Fort; in ten minutes they were in mid-stream. A half mile more to go. But with the water growing choppy and the boat bobbing about, it was difficult to dip the oars, impossible to maintain speed. Joe kept watching the oncoming whitecaps, the approaching darkness with lightning flashes behind the clouds. The waves were now coming in swells, and one of them spilled over the gunwales into the bottom of the boat.

"Take the oars! Quick, Joe! The altar breads, the vestments." Father Neumann lifted the Mass kit from the bottom boards onto the forward seat, swiftly rolled a piece of canvas into a wad and set it under the bow seat; made another wad of his coat, then set the Mass kit on top of both well above the reach of any water that might come into the boat. He put his breviary into his hat and tucked it too under the bow seat.

"Make it fast, Father. The whitecaps are coming. They're here."

Father Neumann grasped the sides to steady himself.

"Come back, come back here. We want the bow out of the water."

Father Neumann made his way back on his knees and just as he passed Joe the first whitecap hit the boat, sending a splash of water over them. Joe was getting frantic.

"Don't panic, Joe, please. Let's say a prayer. You keep rowing."

The prow bit into another whitecap, dashing another splash all over them.

"Hail, Mary, full of grace, the Lord is with thee...." Father Neumann paid no notice to the whitecaps, the churning water. "Star of the Sea...."

"Pray for us," Joe answered. "Aren't you afraid, Father?"

"No. The good God is taking care of us."

Another whitecap split across the prow. Father Neumann was enjoying the bath.

"Get the scoop under the seat, Father, and start bailing out, or we'll be swamped." The bottom now had two inches of water.

With the flat wooden scoop in his hand, Father Neumann paused to figure it out, then took off his shoes and stockings, rolled up his pants and knelt down in the water, the better to handle the bailing business.

Swoosh, a half gallon of water went over the side. Swoosh, another half gallon back into the river. He was enjoying the work. The next whitecap hit the prow, slapping Father Neumann full in the back. Joe started to laugh.

"You look so funny there, Father, with your bare feet and legs in the water." Father laughed, and their laughter mingled with the noise of the waves until another whitecap brought them back to their jobs—Joe to the oars, Father Neumann to the bailing scoop.

Then came the rain, a torrential downpour. Suddenly a blinding flash of lightning that snapped and crackled all around the boat followed by a deafening crash of thunder. Joe turned sickly white. Father Neumann made the sign of the cross over Joe. "Thanks be to God," he said.

Joe looked at Father Neumann in frank surprise. "Thanks be to God that we weren't hit." Joe blessed himself.

The next flash of lightning was well up the river. With the downpour of rain the wind died down and the whitecaps subsided. The summer storm passed as quickly as it had come and the sun peered over the edge of the black clouds.

"Weren't you afraid, Father?"

"No, Joe. God was in the center of that lightning, watching over us."

Across the river they could see their landing beach where two men were waiting with a farm wagon. Father Neumann sat on the stern seat and began to put on his stockings and shoes.

"But why, Father? They are all soaking wet."

"When I meet my people I must be dressed like a priest, not like a little boy who is playing in the water."

They both laughed, and their laughter rang over the dancing waves.

Years after, Joe Soler, then an old man, loved to tell his grandchildren the story of Father Neumann and the storm on the Patapsco.

EPISODE 12

Mother Theresa, S.S.N.D.

The Christian education of children was of great concern to Father Neumann all during his priestly life. As a young pastor on the Niagara frontier, as the Rector in Pittsburgh and in Baltimore, he gave of his time and energy in improving Catholic schools.

But the parish schools of those days, where they did exist, were often hit or miss affairs conducted in church basements or rectories by good pious ladies more willing than competent.

When he was appointed the Vice-Provincial of the American Redemptorists, his first priority was to raise the teaching standard of the seven parochial schools under his jurisdiction. Divine Providence unexpectedly placed in his hands the solution to the problem of good religious teachers.

In the summer of 1847 Mother Theresa and a group of five Notre Dame School Sisters left Munich enroute to the United States to open a school and new Motherhouse at St. Mary's in northwestern Pennsylvania. On arrival in New York City she was surprised to learn that St. Mary's would never be suitable for a Motherhouse, much less a convent. Disappointed but not discouraged she decided to continue on to St. Mary's by way of Baltimore where she could consult with Father Neumann who had several priests working in the colony.

Father Neumann received the Sisters warmly and approved of their plans to open schools in the United States, but cautioned Mother Theresa that St. Mary's was almost impossible. It was too far removed from everything and so poor that settlers were leaving every day.

But if Mother Theresa would care to consider it, he had an alternative. The Redemptorists had charge of three schools in Baltimore—St. James, St. Michael's and St. Alphonsus—which were sadly in need of trained religious teachers. Mother Theresa accepted the proposal, and it was agreed that the next day they would go to see the Archbishop and lay the matter before him.

Archbishop Eccleston was most gracious to the Sisters and approved of Mother Theresa's zeal for Catholic education. But Father Neumann's plan presented a difficulty. Sound financial backing was an absolute necessity. Overburdened himself with debts, he could offer no help.

"Can't you see, Father Neumann, that without financial backing the plan is untenable? Sorry to say this, Mother Theresa, but I cannot and will not grant you permission to open a foundation in the Archdiocese."

...The afternoon sun was sinking over the green hills of northwestern Pennsylvania. Mother Theresa and four nuns seated on boards in an open farm wagon were on the last stretch of the journey to St. Mary's. Baron von Schroeter, the agent for the colony, sat up front with the driver.

Dusk deepened on the forest trail, and a chill dampness rose from the earth. Swarms of mosquitoes disturbed by the oncoming wagon wheels rose from the underbrush and like dive bombers took to the air. The barking of a wolf came from the depths of the forest. The Sisters began to shiver. For three days now they had been floundering through this wilderness of trees.

"Baron, how much further?" Sister Maria's voice was weak from hunger and fatigue.

"Sisters," announced the Baron turning around, "we are almost there. See the daylight ahead? That's it."

The Baron rose in his seat and fired three shots in the air, the signal to the settlers that they were arriving.

The sight that met their eyes left the Sisters speechless. St. Mary's was not a city, not even a village, but a collection of rough houses, shanties and log cabins set back near the edge of the forest with meager truck gardens planted between stumps of fallen trees. The Baron explained that the rich farmlands were further along.

People began coming along the road, out of the forest, from the houses and cabins and crowded around their wagon: tall gaunt men, listless women with babes in arms, ragged children with faces looking up to the Sisters. The pitiful look in their big eager eyes, the thin tight mouths seemed to regard the Sisters so hopefully. Tears rolled down Mother Theresa's face.

A mad shout went up when she spoke a few words to the crowd—the men yelled, the boys cheered and clapped.

A pathway opened through the crowd to allow two Redemptorist priests through. After a hearty supper in the rectory, the priests took the Sisters to the rustic chapel for a visit and left them in their new convent, a rough four-room cottage like the others with a wooden cross on the door.

On their hard cots the Sisters fell fast asleep. But not Mother Theresa. Too exhausted to sleep, her thoughts raced on. Her disappointments and trials gave way to new plans and dreams. After a few days rest, she would travel on alone to Pittsburgh to let the bishop know of her arrival in his diocese. Then back to Baltimore. But first she would start a new school here in the wilderness for the children who had looked up into her heart at the side of the wagon.

Mother Theresa arrived back in Baltimore exhausted, disappointed and discouraged. The Bishop of Pittsburgh was offended with her for coming to St. Mary's. Archbishop Eccleston had refused permission for the Notre Dame Sisters to settle in Baltimore. Her dreams of a new Motherhouse in the United States lay shattered. Nothing was left but to return home to Munich. But first she must visit Father Neumann in St. Alphonsus Rectory to thank him for his kindness to the Sisters.

Father Neumann did not at first recognize the three nuns waiting for him in the rectory parlor, dressed as they were in secular travel clothes. They had become so thin and haggard that he had difficulty concealing his shock. In the two short months since he had seen her, Mother Theresa's hair had turned gray.

"Welcome back, Mother Theresa," he said, trying to be cheerful. "I'm glad to see you again, back in Baltimore."

Mother Theresa clasped his outstretched hand in both her hands.

"Father Neumann, I'm so glad to be back." Her words came slowly and with effort. "St. Mary's was just impossible as a Motherhouse. Baron von Schroeter had deceived us with his glowing words. But I have left two sisters there, Sister Maria and Sister Seraphine to care for those poor children. And Sister Emmanuela—" tears choked her words and she broke down. Sister Caroline explained that Sister Emmanuela had died on the journey and lay buried in Harrisburg in a nameless grave.

"God rest her brave soul," murmured Father Neumann. "Mother, God has tried you severely. He must have great things in store."

"And to think, Father," continued Mother Theresa drying her eyes with a handkerchief, "to think that I entered the Pittsburgh diocese without canonical permission. I feel terrible. Baron von Schroeter had assured me that the legalities had been cleared. And now the Baron has disappeared with all our funds."

Sorrow and silence gripped the little rectory parlor. Human nature could stand no more. Father Neumann was lost for words. The ringing of the community bell inside the monastery broke the silence.

"Mother," said Father Neumann, "God cannot ignore the tears of His servants. Now listen to the good news. After you left here for St. Mary's, I went back to see Archbishop Eccleston. He has reversed his decision."

Mother Theresa gasped and dropped her handkerchief. What was he trying to say? Was she hearing correctly?

"Yes, Sisters, the Archbishop has given you permission for the new Motherhouse, and I am allowed to hand over to your care our three parish schools in Baltimore."

Neumann Center, Philadelphia, Pa.

This was too much. Mother Theresa began to cry again, but for joy.

"And what is more, I have the ideal place for your Motherhouse, our former House of Novitiate with its beautiful gardens next to St. James Church on Aisquith Street.

Mother Theresa knelt and kissed Father Neumann's hand. Sister Caroline cried on the shoulder of Sister Magdalene.

"Mother, please, wait a while." He raised Mother Theresa to her feet. "I have a confession to make. True, the Archbishop did give permission but on one condition—that he would not be financially responsible. I assured him that I would be responsible." Father Neumann paused, lost in his own thoughts. "Mother, I wanted you and the good Sisters so badly that I spoke too quickly, I fear. The cold truth is that the Redemptorists have overexpanded, and we are now deep in debt, almost bankrupt and my priests are living from hand to mouth. Like Peter walking on the water, I feel I am beginning to sink."

This admission coming from a priest of such outward calm took Mother Theresa by surprise. How deeply he must be suffering. Her own trials seemed to grow lighter, and a sudden confidence sparkled in her eyes.

"And, Father, the good Lord, like He did to Peter, will stretch out His Hand to you and me. True, you are deep in debt and we are destitute. But, Father, I have a good friend back home. Before we left for America, King Louis of Bavaria said that if ever I needed help, I should write to him. Father Neumann, we need his help right now."

In due time, Mother Theresa received from good King Louis a bankdraft for a handsome sum of money which provided not only for all her needs but also allowed her to purchase from the Redemptorists the former Novitiate on Aisquith Street.

Mother Theresa now had her new Motherhouse, a home for future Sisters and a cradle for new vocations, while Father Neumann, relieved of his most pressing debts, had a fruitful source of co-workers in the field of Catholic education.

EPISODE 13

Sick Call to Elkridge Landing

Elkridge Landing, as it was then known, was a settlement of German farmers, five miles west of Baltimore. When Father Neumann learned that they were without priest or chapel, he took it on himself to visit them regularly to say Mass and to administer the Sacraments. A Marcus Breuning became his helper and contact man.

Late one afternoon the door bell rang insistently in the corridor of St. Alphonsus Rectory. In the parlor Father Neumann found a trembling girl with tears running down her cheeks. "Father Neumann," she gasped. "Come quick. Dad is dying. He keeps asking for you."

He put his hand on her trembling shoulders and wiped the tears from her eyes. "Tell me where you live."

"You know me, Father. I'm Anna Breuning."

"Ah, yes," he said, "the daughter of Marcus Breuning of Elkridge Landing." Marcus was trying to raise four motherless children. Anna, twelve, was the oldest.

"How did you come, Anna?" He was puzzled. There was no public conveyance.

"I drove here, Father. The horse and buggy are waiting outside at the curbstone."

This was incredible. Elkridge Landing was a long hard drive for such a small girl.

"God bless you, Anna," he said softly.

"Please, Father. The horse and buggy are waiting outside at the door."

"Don't worry, Anna," he said. "Wait for me outside, ready to go. I'll be out in a few minutes. The Brother will bring a bucket of water for the horse. I'll have the Blessed Sacrament. So, no talking on the way."

On busy Saratoga Street horse and buggy went rattling over the cobblestones, Father Neumann grasping the reins, Anna clutching the edge of the seat. Anna was afraid for the first time. They left the city limits and rolled onto the smooth dirt roads of the countryside. When the horse, sniffing the clean cool air, gave an impatient tug on the reins, Father Neumann slackened the reins with an encouraging slap on its rump. The horse broke into a smart trot. Houses and barns passed swiftly by. Shaded woods and open fields were left behind. Now the horse was beginning to tire out.

Holding the reins in his left hand he took out his Rosary, placed his hand over the Blessed Sacrament in his inside pocket and moved his lips in silent prayer. Anna watched him, entranced by the heavenly calm on his face. The decades slipped slowly through his fingers. Anna grew nervous. Her father was dying, and here was Father Neumann calmly praying as if there were no hurry.

"Please, Father," she whispered, "can't you gallop the horse? Dad may not hold out."

Father Neumann paused, held the Rosary up and said, "The Blessed Mother will see that we get there in time. Now let's finish the Rosary together, out loud." Anna was reassured.

They crossed the bridge over the Patapsco River and pulled into the Breuning farm in good time. The dying man gave a sigh of relief on seeing the priest enter the room. Father Neumann heard the good man's confession and reassured him as to the safety of his four children. Marcus Breuning received Holy Communion, and with the children kneeling at his bedside resigned his soul into the hands of His Creator.

EPISODE 14

Expelled from School

The School Sisters of Notre Dame in the beginning were given charge of three schools in Baltimore, but Mother Theresa had only three Sisters. She took over St. Michael's School. Sister Magdalene was assigned to St. James' School next to the new Motherhouse on Aisquith Street; Sister Caroline, who later became Mother Superior in the United States, would set out each morning across town to St. Alphonsus' School on Saratoga Street. Father Neumann was at that time Rector of St. Alphonsus.

One evening after supper Father Neumann was in his room, writing by candle light the notes for the new Children's Catechism which he was preparing for the publisher when a soft knock came on his door.

"Ave Maria," he called out. "Come in, Brother Aloysius." He knew the knock. The door opened and Brother Aloysius waited on the threshold. He had a deep respect for his holy Rector.

"What is it, Brother?" Father Neumann continued writing.

"I don't like to disturb you, Father Rector. But there's a Mr. Bayer in the parlor to see you. He seems troubled."

"No disturbance. Call me any time, Brother, night or day. Tell Mr. Bayer I'll see him in a moment."

He wiped the pen clean of ink, shuffled his papers and placed them neatly in the table drawer. Mr. Bayer was probably another of his poor parishioners, immigrants for the most part, who had to labor long and hard just to make a meager living. How his heart went out to these poor faithful people!

In the parlor he found Mr. Bayer, his strong hands resting on the edge of the table, his head bent down in dejection.

"Mr. Bayer, I presume?" Father Neumann's voice was soft and tender.

Mr. Bayer looked up slowly and rose to his feet. Father Neumann took the chair opposite and motioned Mr. Bayer to be seated.

"Father Neumann, it's about my boy, James," Mr. Bayer began.

"Oh yes, I have James in religion class," replied Father Neumann. James Bayer was the tall boy who sat in the back of Sister Caroline's class.

"I work hard all day long, Father, just to earn enough to keep my family, and here I come home tonight and find another note from Sister Caroline." Mr. Bayer paused. "Please, Father Neumann, don't let my boy be expelled from St. Alphonsus' School."

Expelled? Father Neumann did not answer. Expulsion from a Catholic school was only for the incorrigible, for those who had a bad influence on the other pupils. He did not believe in expulsion. In such a vital matter, as Rector of the parish, he should have been consulted. Yet he could not blame Sister Caroline. She was doing remarkable work in reorganizing the school and could not be expected to think of all the angles while trying to supervise the teachers and teach a class of children unaccustomed to order and discipline.

"I tell you what, Mr. Bayer." He placed his hands over the rough, hardened hands of Mr. Bayer. "You and I, we will leave the whole matter in God's hands. Just go home now to your family and before you go to bed say a fervent prayer to St. Joseph, the patron of families. Tomorrow morning I'll try to see Sister Caroline."

The children had been restless all morning. Sister Caroline did not understand it. Perhaps fresh air might help. She had one of the taller boys open the windows from the top and to create circulation she opened the classroom door.

"Now, boys and girls," she announced, "take a sheet of clean paper. Instead of oral spelling we'll have a written test of today's lesson." Paper work, she thought, might help the children concentrate. The lesson for that day was words spelled with either EI or IE. She dictated slowly.

"believe – receive – receipt – cashier – deceive – relieve."

Looking over the class she noticed a strange movement at the back of the room. James Bayer's head waved up and down, up and down, at each word she gave. She moved slowly across the front of the room, down the side aisle. From this angle she saw it plainly, the open book on the lap of James Bayer. She continued dictating. Suddenly she raised her voice.

"RETRIEVE. James Bayer, spell the word aloud."

The boy looked up in alarm. Had Sister Caroline seen the book on his lap? He shoved his knees further under the desk.

"James, stand up and spell 'retrieve.'"

A smirk curled the boy's lips. "I can't. My knees are stuck under the desk." The mockery in his voice caused all heads to turn back.

"Stand up, James Bayer." The authority in her voice gave the boy no choice.

He stepped into the aisle and the book clattered to the floor. The girl across the aisle picked up the book—his *spelling book*—and placed it on his desk. The children gasped. Several boys in back, friends of James Bayer, snickered aloud. Sister Caroline turned pale and hesitated.

"James Bayer," she said with an ominous softness, "spell the word I asked for."

"I won't." This was open defiance in front of the whole class.

"Did you study last night?" Sister was parrying for time.

"Nope!"

"And why not?" Sister Caroline was making no progress.

"I just didn't feel like it." He was shouting.

"I am sorry to be compelled to do this." Sister addressed the whole class. "James Bayer is hereby expelled from St. Alphonsus' School. He will take his cap and coat and leave immediately."

The boy got to his feet with a deliberate slowness, grabbed his things from the peg in back, snapped the cap on his head and scuffed up the aisle, dragging his coat on the floor. Then he stopped suddenly when he saw Father Neumann standing in the open doorway.

Father Neumann gave no sign of recognition. It was too late, much too late now. Such deep defiance must have smoldered for a long time. Poor Sister Caroline. How brave she had been.

Bishop Neumann's
Gift to America...
The Parochial School System

"James," Father Neumann said. "You heard what Sister said." He stepped aside, the boy removed his cap and passed on.

Father Neumann gave Sister Caroline a smile of sympathy and followed the boy down the corridor.

Some weeks later Father Neumann was teaching the religion class. Sister Caroline, sitting at a desk in the back of the room, marvelled at the way he had with children. True sorrow for sin—how natural it sounded on his lips, and the simplicity with which he told the story of the Prodigal Son held the children spellbound.

Unnoticed by anyone there came a soft knock on the classroom door. At the second knock a boy in the front seat opened the door and stepped back with a surprised gasp. There stood James Bayer, his hair neatly parted, hugging his cap to his chest. Father Neumann stopped the story.

"Father Neumann," the boy's voice was slow and clear, "may I please come back to school?"

"James, you must ask permission from Sister Caroline." He motioned to Sister Caroline at the back. Sister Caroline walked up the aisle and looked inquiringly from the boy to Father Neumann.

"Sister, I should have told you that James and I, for the past three weeks—" He turned to the boy. "Three weeks, wasn't it, James?"

"Four weeks, Father."

The love and veneration in the boy's face was a revelation to Sister Caroline.

"For four weeks, Sister, James and I have had daily sessions in the Rectory. We have done some honest thinking and a great deal of serious studying. I can guarantee you, Sister, that if you take James back, you will never have cause for regrets."

"I apologize, Sister Caroline. I'm sorry for what I did." This was a new boy, a changed James Bayer.

Tears of joy glistened in Sister Caroline's eyes.

"James, I'm so glad to have you back." She turned to Father Neumann, "and I'm more than grateful to you, Father. This is just too wonderful."

A twinkle leaped in Father Neumann's deep dark eyes. "Let's see now, Sister. I usually have a bag of candy in my pocket. Let's celebrate." He pulled a brown bag from his pocket. Then, as if it were a mere accident: "Now, isn't this strange! Today I seem to have two bags of candy, enough for the whole class."

The boys and girls laughed and clapped as James Bayer took his seat. The *prodigal son* had returned.

EPISODE 15

The Pectoral Cross

Archbishop Kenrick had been to confession that afternoon. It was such a consolation to confess to good Father Neumann, the holy Rector of St. Alphonsus Church. The Archbishop went along the rectory corridor to the community chapel to say his penance in the presence of the Blessed Sacrament. Before leaving for home he knocked at Father Neumann's door.

"I'm back again, Father Rector," he said. "May I come in a while?"

"Certainly, Your Excellency," said Father Neumann, offering the Archbishop his chair and closing the door.

"It's about a little matter—I should say a rather serious problem of administration. I need advice."

As the Archbishop presented the problem with its ramifications, Father Neumann sat on the edge of his cot, listening intently, and now and then interjecting a question.

"So," concluded the Archbishop, "that is how matters stand. I just don't know which way to turn, what to decide."

Father Neumann said nothing for a full minute. Then he raised his deep dark eyes and looked straight into the face of his Archbishop.

Most Rev. Francis P. Kenrick
Archbishop of Baltimore 1851-1863

"Your Grace," he said, "this is how I would solve it." While Father Neumann presented his solution, Archbishop Kenrick had to marvel at Father Neumann's uncanny way of penetrating to the essentials, at his deep knowledge of human nature, at his unerring application of the pertinent Code of Canon Law.

"Marvelous," the Archbishop exclaimed. "It all seems so simple the way you put it. Thanks be to God." Then he added half in jest, "Don't you know, I think you should be a bishop yourself."

Father Neumann recoiled in horror. His memory flashed back to the horrible dream he had had as a Redemptorist Novice.

"Yes," repeated the Archbishop teasingly with an Irish twinkle in his eye. "You would make a good bishop yourself."

From St. Alphonsus Rectory to the Baltimore Cathedral was a short walk. But the weather was so mild Archbishop Kenrick decided to go for a good long walk. Exercise and fresh air seemed to stimulate the thinking process and he had many problems to think out. One of them was the selection of a new bishop for the vacant See of Philadelphia. As he headed north on Calvert Street, no one seemed to recognize him, for which he was grateful.

As metropolitan of the Baltimore Province it was his duty, as well as that of his four suffragan bishops, to help select candidates for the See of Philadelphia, to make out lists of three suitable candidates, a *terna* as it is called, and forward them to Rome for the final selection.

Since his transfer to Baltimore, Philadelphia had been without a bishop. That was for six months. Many names had been suggested to him, many names he felt he had to discard for one reason or another. He had finally settled on two names, Father Edward Purcell and Father William Elder, eminently worthy priests, both of them. But Archbishop Kenrick felt that neither one was fully qualified to meet the various needs of Philadelphia. How well he knew those needs after having served in Philadelphia first as coadjutor bishop and Ordinary for twenty-one years.

His last words to Father Neumann came back to him, "You should be a bishop yourself," this time not as a thoughtless jest but as a distinct possibility.

The Archbishop found an empty bench near the Washington Monument and sat down, thrilled by the new possibility. The more he considered Neumann, the more he became convinced that Divine Providence had placed the right man in his path, in his own backyard, you might say.

Father John Neumann was a holy man of God. This was of prime importance where immortal souls are concerned. He was likewise a good administrator. Kenrick could see that in the way he controlled the Germans of St. Alphonsus Parish. In Pittsburgh Father Neumann had accomplished the impossible in building the beautiful Gothic structure of St. Philomena's Church. Philadelphia's Cathedral was half finished and stood there a sorry spectacle. Philadelphia had a long standing problem with trusteeism. The Redemptorists were noted for their successful handling of the issue. Neumann himself had settled several such cases. Most of all, Neumann was beloved by all with whom he came in contact. Father Neumann seemed to have exactly what Kenrick wanted. True, he was no great preacher in the pulpit, and he was shy in social circles, but what did this matter where souls were concerned? The name of Father John

Neumann must be the first name on the *terna* to be sent to Rome. Archbishop Kenrick returned home that evening in high spirits.

After a good supper Archbishop Kenrick penned letters to his four suffragan bishops telling them the good news and urging them to complete the *terna* to be sent to Rome. Bishop Reynolds of Charleston replied, congratulating the Archbishop for his choice of Neumann, adding that he himself had come to the same decision. But Bishop O'Connor of Pittsburgh wrote back in no uncertain terms stating that Neumann would be a good choice for some smaller diocese like Erie, but never for such a prestigious See as Philadelphia: he lacked pulpit eloquence and was inept at social contacts. Bishop McGill of Richmond opposed the choice of Neumann for the same reasons, while Bishop Whelan of Wheeling, West Virginia, heartily approved of Neumann, adding that his gift of attracting people would be of paramount importance in such a diversified diocese as Philadelphia. Kenrick likewise asked other archbishops of the U.S. to submit *terna* to Rome. The process of selection rolled into high gear. Kenrick was happy, hoping and praying that Neumann would be the final choice.

After confession one week, Archbishop Kenrick strongly suggested to Father Neumann that he should prepare his soul for the responsibility of a bishopric. Father Neumann became frightened and alarmed. The Archbishop was not teasing this time. In desperation he confided the matter to his Father Provincial, beseeching him on his knees to do all in his power to block the move to make him a bishop. On his weekly visits to the various convents to hear confession, he asked the nuns to pray for his special intention, "to avert," as he phrased it, "a great calamity from the Catholic Church in America." He had the Fathers and brothers of St. Alphonsus' community add the Seven Penitential Psalms after night prayers.

Father Provincial wrote a strong letter to the Superior General in Vienna, who in turn wrote a letter to the Procurator in Rome. The Procurator quietly took the two letters to his good friend at Propaganda, Cardinal Altieri.

Archbishop Kenrick, on his part, after forwarding his list of names to Propaganda sent a secret letter to his friend, the Rector of the Irish College in Rome, who in turn quietly presented Kenrick's letter to Monsignor Barnabo, secretary of Propaganda. The battle was on.

In December, 1851, the Sacred Congregation of Propaganda Fide met in full council to make its final choice of the next bishop of Philadelphia. When the various *terna* were opened, there was a wide divergence of names, no clear consensus though two names seemed to predomiate, those of John Neumann and Edward Purcell.

Cardinal Altieri took the floor and with cogent reasoning strongly opposed naming Neumann: first, because Neumann did not want to be a bishop. So why waste the dignity on one who would like to refuse it? Secondly, his Redemptorist Superiors were loathe to lose his services. Cardinal Altieri won over four cardinals to his side; the others were unimpressed.

Monsignor Barnabo, armed with Kenrick's letter, had done his homework. Who better than Kenrick knew the needs of Philadelphia and who was in a better position to know the candidate he had proposed? When the final tally was counted, the majority of the cardinals had voted for John Neumann as the next bishop of Philadelphia.

The final vote was forwarded to the Holy Father, together with the two letters from Neumann's Redemptorist Superiors. The final decision now rested with the Holy Father, Pope Pius IX. The good news leaked back to Baltimore to Archbishop Kenrick, who in turn advised his confessor to begin thinking of getting himself a pectoral cross and ring.

On returning to his room one evening Father Neumann saw on his table something that seemed to sparkle in the twilight. He lit the candle. There in the center of the table neatly arranged in a circle was a gold chain with a gold cross in the middle and a big signet ring with a sparkling emerald, the insignia of a bishop. He turned pale and trembled. He hurried along the corridor in a daze.

"Brother," he demanded of the brother porter, "has anyone been in my room?"

"Yes, Father Rector, the Archbishop." He was frightened at the look on his Rector's face. "I thought he was going to confession."

Without a word Father Neumann staggered back to his room and turned the key in the lock. The pectoral cross and the ring—he swept them into the table drawer and fell on his knees beside the cot. "O my God, why have You done this to me?" He buried his head in the pillow. "All I asked You," he gasped, "was to persevere—as a good Redemptorist." He began to sob like a child. "A Redemptorist." John Neumann was going through his Gethsemani.

He was not present in chapel for the evening meditation; his place at supper was empty. The Fathers were puzzled. He was home, they knew. The brother porter thought it prudent to say nothing: serious business was afoot. The Father Minister knocked on the Rector's room after night prayers, asking through the closed door if he were sick. After a long pause came the answer that he only wanted to be alone for a while.

Later that night when all the Fathers and brothers had retired to their rooms, Father Neumann came out and went to the chapel where he spent the whole night beseeching his Lord by some miracle to spare him the terrifying responsibility of the bishopric. Slowly, calmness returned to his tortured soul. When the community came to chapel early next morning for meditation, they found their beloved rector in his usual place kneeling erect, ready to begin the morning prayer.

Archbishop Kenrick returned to St. Alphonsus' later that morning and asked the brother to ring the community bell and have the Fathers all assemble in the chapel. Then he went directly to Father Neumann's room and shut the door.

Surprise spread through the Rectory corridors. Why the bell at this hour? When the brother porter explained, all filed silently to the chapel, the novices, the brothers and the priests of the parish. Archbishop Kenrick and Father Neumann took the last pew.

"Fathers and brothers," he explained, "I have brought you here for some very important news. But first let someone intone the hymn *Veni Creator Spiritus.*" At the last verse the Archbishop went to the altar, took out a long envelope from the fold in his soutane, unfolded a document and read it aloud in Latin. It was the Papal Bull, naming Rev. John N. Neumann, C.SS.R., as the new bishop of Philadelphia. On the bottom were added the words "under obedience and without appeal." The Pope had spoken, his but to obey.

On March 28, 1852, before a capacity crowd in St. Alphonsus Church, Rev. John Nepomucene Neumann, C.SS.R., was solemnly consecrated by Archbishop Francis P. Kenrick as the fourth bishop of Philadelphia. The struggle was over; calm and peace had returned to the soul of Father Neumann. Strengthened by the grace of the Sacrament, he was determined with the help of Almighty God and the wise counsel of his predecessor to carry on the work for immortal souls in the diocese of Philadelphia.

EPISODE 16

Margaret's Marble Statue

Four small girls went chattering along Chestnut Street one afternoon with an envelope for the Bishop of Philadelphia.

"And," said little Margaret McSheffery to the others, "Sister said we must not stay long. The Bishop is a busy man."

On Logan Square they opened the picket gate to the Bishop's Residence, skipped up the front stairs, pulled the bells and walked in. Across the lobby beneath a framed picture of the Blessed Mother, a small marble sculpture rested on a low table. The girls went directly to the statue.

"Here he is," said Margaret. "Ain't he cute?"

The girls clustered around an exquisite white statue of a baby curled up asleep in a sea shell.

"Is he the Infant Jesus?" one girl wanted to know.

Margaret did not think so because the Infant Jesus always slept on straw in a manger.

The girls dropped to their knees and gazed reverently on the face of the sleeping baby. Bishop Neumann came down the staircase in his black Redemptorist habit wearing his pectoral cross and paused midway down, intrigued by the rapt attention of his little visitors.

"Well, little ladies," he said approaching the group, "what do you think of my statue? Isn't it beautiful?" The statue was a gift from a dear friend in Europe. The girls rose to their feet and turned to the Bishop.

"Would you like to have him?" he asked, reading their thoughts.

Four pair of eyes danced in eager anticipation.

"I'll tell you what," he said half in banter. "The one who can carry it may take it home." He knew the marble statue was too heavy for their little arms.

Margaret, taking the bishop at his word, tried to lift it and though it was only twelve inches high could not move it from its base. The other girls tried and tried again, but the statue refused to be moved. At the look of disappointment on their faces, the bishop felt sorry for them and regretted that he had played with their feelings. He should have known how literally children take things.

But Margaret was not one to give up easily. She passed the envelope from the Sisters to the Bishop, and while he was opening it, she slipped quietly out the front door. Bishop Neumann read the message, then read it again. The Sisters had difficulty about the rent on the house they were using as a temporary convent. He folded the message and looked at the girls. Where had Margaret gone? Just then he heard a thumping sound as of something being dragged up the front steps. The door swung open and in stalked Margaret pulling a small cart with which to carry home the Bishop's statue. Margaret McSheffery had outwitted the Bishop of Philadelphia.

Bishop Neumann could not hide his surprise. Margaret really wanted possession of his statue, and he had no heart to refuse her. Perhaps this was

Margaret's Marble Statue

God's way of asking him to detach his affections from things of this earth. A slow smile creased the corners of his mouth, and he gave a loud, hearty laugh.

But Margaret could see no reason for merriment. The Bishop in all seriousness placed the statue carefully in Margaret's wagon and helped the girls ease the precious load down the front stairs to the sidewalk.

Margaret turned to the gate to thank the good Bishop. His deep, dark eyes looked piercingly into her smiling Irish eyes and he said, "God keep you, Margaret. Some day you will become a Holy Cross Sister." He paused, "And then you will become the Mother General."

Margaret McSheffery treasured the Bishop's statue all her life both as Sister Mary Annunciata and later as the elected Mother General of the Holy Cross Sisters. Today that marble statue of a baby curled up asleep in a seashell stands a treasured heirloom in the Archives of the Motherhouse of the Holy Cross Sisters in Notre Dame, Indiana.

EPISODE 17

Moyamensing Prison

Bishop Neumann's top priority on becoming Bishop of Philadelphia was to get to know his priests and his people. The first week he visited the convents and religious houses and then started the canonical visitation of all the city parishes.

At lunch one day after a busy morning of confirming the children of the parish, the pastor brought up the subject of the Skrupinski brothers. The Philadelphia newspapers were full of the lurid details of the murder, the trial and the final verdict condemning the two brothers to death. They were then in Moyamensing Prison awaiting the gallows. Several priests had gone to the prison to try to persuade them to go to confession, only to be repulsed. The two brothers were hardened sinners. Bishop Neumann was touched not so much by the horror of the crime as by their refusal to be reconciled to God. He considered it his duty, as their chief pastor, to try again to bring them back to the Mercy of God.

He left the Rectory that afternoon accompanied by his Vicar General, Father Edward Sourin, to make a visit to the Skrupinski brothers.

"Are you sure, Bishop," asked Father Sourin, "that you want to go through with this?"

"Father," replied Bishop Neumann, "where souls are concerned, the Good Shepherd does not hesitate. Let us say the Rosary on the way."

The Bishop and the Vicar General walked on in silence, fingering the rosaries in their pockets.

Moyamensing Prison was an imposing edifice built of granite blocks. They went up the stairs to the main entrance and crossed the lobby to the warden's office. The warden came to the counter.

"Warden," said Father Sourin, "I would like to introduce you to our new Bishop of Philadelphia, Right Reverend John Neumann."

The warden, a non-Catholic, was visibly unimpressed.

"Warden," put in Bishop Neumann, "our purpose today is to ask your permission to visit two condemned men who are Catholics."

"Catholics," sneered the warden. "You mean the two murderers who..." Bishop Neumann interrupted.

"Your pardon, Warden, I am not interested in what they have done, God forgive them, but in the future of their souls."

"Take my advice, Sir, and go home. Several of your priests have already tried—to their sorrow."

"Nonetheless, I must see them. I am their bishop," insisted Bishop Neumann.

The warden agreed to let the bishop in, provided he did not further disturb the two men. Bishop Neumann assured him that there would be no disturbance.

The turnkey led the group through numerous doors and barred gates, unlocking and relocking each with a chilling clank—along the long bricked corridor of the main cell block to "solitary confinement," an isolated row of cells.

The warden rapped with his gun handle on the bars of cell n. 3.

"Get up, Joe," he shouted, "you have visitors today."

Burly and bewhiskered Joe rolled off his bunk and with his back to the "visitors" stretched and yawned. Then, in his own good time, he turned to have a good look. For a moment he hesitated when he saw the little bishop and his eyes rolled in fright, a fright that told Bishop Neumann all he needed to know, that faith was not yet dead in the heart of the man.

But Joe rallied quickly and with a bitter laugh kicked viciously at the wall of the next cell.

"Get up, Stan," he yelled. "Get up and see what's here to convert us. More...priests, two of them this time. You handle the tall one."

Joe cleared his throat, came close to the bars and spat straight into the Bishop's face, then folded his arms and stepped back to see how he liked it. His jaw dropped in dumb amazement when he saw the little bishop calmly take out his handkerchief and without the least resentment wipe the spittle from his cheek. Stan in the next cell was watching through the bars.

"Warden," Bishop Neumann's voice was soft and deep. "Would you and Father Sourin mind waiting outside? Joe and I would like to be alone."

Outside in the main cell block, Father Sourin, the warden and the turnkey waited. For five minutes no word passed between them. Prisoners in nearby cells grasped the steel bars and watched. Ten minutes passed. The warden pulled out his watch. Fifteen minutes and still no knowing what was going on behind the door. Then came a gentle tap on the door and when the turnkey opened it, Bishop Neumann glided out like a man in a trance.

"Are you all right, Your Excellency?" Father Sourin asked, bending over his bishop.

"How wonderful are the works of the Lord," he murmured. "Praised forever be the great Mercy of our God! Stan and Joe have come back to the fold."

The warden did not quite understand what was going on.

"Warden," said Bishop Neumann, "you will have no more trouble from Joe and Stan. Do try to be extra nice to the poor boys."

The warden grasped Bishop Neumann's hand and thanked him over and over.

"And with your permission," Bishop Neumann continued, "I'd like to send a priest to give them the Sacraments and to be with them till the end."

Through the gentle pastor of souls two hardened sinners had come back to the fold of the Good Shepherd.

EPISODE 18

The Sisters of St. Francis

In October, 1854, Pope Pius IX invited all the Bishops of the Catholic World to come to Rome to assist at the promulgation of the dogma of Mary's Immaculate Conception. Bishop Neumann was overjoyed. Mary's Immaculate Conception had long been a firm belief with him. He wrote back to Rome gladly accepting the invitation, requesting at the same time an audience with the Holy Father for his official "ad limina" visit. This visit to Rome would afford him a much needed rest after the past two years of intensive activity. Parishes had been started, churches built and as if by magic parochial schools sprang up throughout the diocese. This must all go into his official report to the Holy Father.

Across St. Peter's Square in Rome, Bishop John Neumann in a long black mantle and broad-brimmed Roman hat made his way through the groups of visitors on his way to see the Pope for his first official visit as Bishop of Philadelphia. He passed between the towering columns of Bramante's colonnade and crossed the courtyard to the Papal Quarters.

Two Swiss Guards accosted him, bowed and escorted him to an office and presented him to a young monsignor who examined his credentials.

"Everything is in order, Your Excellency. The Holy Father is expecting you. Leave your mantle and hat here and follow me."

Preceded by the two Papal Guards, Bishop Neumann in purple cassock and the monsignor mounted the long marble staircase. The vast beauty was breathtaking to the little bishop from Philadelphia. The deference shown him was embarrassing. On the top-most landing they waited outside the carved oaken doors of the Papal Library. The doors were opened and an archbishop came out.

"Now," prompted the monsignor, "just do everything I do. Three double genuflections as we approach the throne."

At the far end of the Papal Library, the Holy Father, Pope Pius IX, in a cream white cassock and cape sat on a low throne flanked by Church dignitaries of the Propaganda. Neumann went down on two knees and bowed.

"And who is this humble little bishop?" the Pope asked his private secretary.

"An American, Your Holiness," whispered the secretary. "Bishop John Neumann of Philadelphia."

"Yes, I recall," smiled the Holy Father. "The Redemptorist from Baltimore who tried so hard not to be a bishop."

The monsignor and Bishop Neumann kissed the cross on the Pope's slipper, then the fisherman's ring on his hand.

"Do rise, Your Excellency, and be seated. We were happy that you could come for the glorious occasion. It was a pleasure to have you hold the book while we proclaimed the dogma of Mary's Immaculate Conception."

He Promoted The
Veneration
of The
Immaculate
Conception

"Your Holiness," replied Bishop Neumann, "it was an honor I shall remember the rest of my life."

"We have received your official report of the diocese." The Cardinal Prefect of Propaganda handed the Pope Neumann's handwritten report. The Holy Father read the summation. "This is most extraordinary, Your Excellency. Thirty-five new parochial schools and twenty-five new churches in two short years. And you wanted to refuse the bishopric. Don't you agree now that obedience is better than sacrifice?"

Bishop Neumann thanked the Holy Father for his encouraging words.

"But, Your Holiness," he added, "I am almost frightened at what must yet be done. Many of my Catholic orphans are being farmed out to strangers and are losing the faith. I must have a Catholic orphanage and special Sisters to take care of them. With your kind permission, I would like to bring over nuns from Germany."

The Pope listened in awe. Such an extraordinary combination of humility and consuming zeal.

"We heartily approve of your plan for an orphanage. But, Bishop, why not start your own congregation of Sisters to take care of this work, an American order?" Bishop Neumann looked into the face of the Holy Father in fright and disbelief. "Yes, Bishop Neumann, we desire you to form an American order of your own and to train them in the principles of religious life. Place them under the patronage of St. Francis of Assisi."

The Pope had spoken. Bishop Neumann had but to obey. Dazed and stupefied, he left the Papal presence, descended the long marble staircase and walked out into the dazzling sunlight of St. Peter's Square.

Pope Pius IX advises
him to establish Franciscan
Nuns of the Third Order
c Neumann Center, Philadelphia, Pa.

What the Pope did not know at the time and Bishop Neumann did not realize was that God had already planted the seed for a new religious order in the hearts of two devout women of Philadelphia.

Miss Barbara Ball had plans to become a Notre Dame teaching Sister, but when her sister, Marie Bachman, was left a widow, Barbara postponed her plans to enter the convent, and went to live with her sister to help support and care for her four fatherless children.

Barbara and Marie by their piety and their charity to the poor of the parish won the respect and love of everyone who knew them. If a child had an earache or an infected wound, he was bundled off to Mrs. Bachman and her medicine closet. Should the mother of a family be confined to a sick bed, Barbara and Marie would take turns caring for the children and cooking the meals. Their work for the poor was a work of love.

One evening after the children had been put to bed and the day's work was done, Marie and Barbara sat in the kitchen in the soft glow of the kerosene lamp, Barbara stitching on the ruffles of a christening dress for a neighbor's new-born baby, Marie darning up the holes in the children's stockings. This was the time of day they both liked best, when they could sit together in the quiet of the night to chat and make plans for the morrow.

"Marie," said Barbara, "I've been thinking." Marie rested the darning needle. "I've been thinking. You know that I have always wanted to consecrate my life to God as a teaching Sister?"

Marie dropped the darning into her lap with a look of fright.

"Since coming here to live and work with you, I have begun to wonder if it were possible to give my life to God in the service of His poor just as we are now doing."

Marie looked closely at her sister. "Barbara," she said. "I've been thinking on the same lines for some time now. And each day I become more convinced that God wants me to give my life to Him in the service of the poor, the sick and the helpless."

How wonderful are the ways of Divine Providence. They both wanted to consecrate their lives to God in the same service. But did an order exist in the States with such a purpose? And would such an order accept a widow with four children? Mother Elizabeth Seton and Mother Cornelia Connelly, both widows, had founded new communities of Sisters to meet new needs. Could Marie and Barbara start a new Congregation? It was agreed that next time they went to confession, Marie would lay the matter before the Rector of St. Peter's.

Father John Hespelein was well acquainted with the work the two ladies were doing for the poor of the parish. But as for starting a new community of Sisters, that was a very serious matter. The prudent thing to do would be to pray much for divine guidance and to wait. As a step toward their goal he suggested that Mrs. Bachman turn her big house into a boarding house for homeless working girls, many of whom were in danger of losing their faith and their virtue.

The Bachman house on Lawrence Street became "Holy Family Home" and was soon occupied by young Catholic working girls. Marie became a second mother to the lonely girls, Barbara their friend and confidante. Under a simple rule of life drawn up by Father Hespelein, peace and piety became the order of the house.

A Miss Anna Dorn heard of the good work being done in Philadelphia and came over from Germany to join the little community. Some of the girls told Mrs. Bachman they wished to quit their jobs and help in the works of charity.

The time was ripe to consult with the Bishop of Philadelphia and to ask his approval. But Bishop Neumann was then in Rome. A letter of petition was sent off to him in Rome, signed by Mrs. Marie Bachman, Barbara Ball, Anna Dorn and by Father John Hespelein.

Bishop Neumann and Father Hespelein left St. Peter's Rectory in Philadelphia and turned south on Lawrence Street.

"Good afternoon, Fathers," said a group of smiling girls stepping off the sidewalk to let them pass.

"Good afternoon, Fathers," cried a group of boys pausing in their game to tip their caps. Bishop Neumann gave them all a smile and a big blessing. Father Hespelein expressed surprise that the children had addressed the bishop as Father.

"Father Hespelein," replied Bishop Neumann, "the highest title anyone can give you or me is that of Father. I love it on the lips of children. Now about your Mrs. Bachman?"

Father Hespelein was at a loss for words to express his admiration for Mrs. Bachman: such solid piety, serene prudence and cheerful poverty. "Bishop, I can only thank God for having brought me into contact with such a holy woman. You will see for yourself."

Number 235 Lawrence Street was a three-story frame house with a neat flower-bed inside the gate. When Father Hespelein raised the knocker and rapped twice, the door was opened by a pleasant young woman in black with a gingham work apron.

"Why, Father Hespelein. And Bishop Neumann. Our home is indeed honored this afternoon." She took their hats and coats.

Barbara Ball came in from the kitchen with two extra chairs.

The room was bare of furniture except for a few chairs and a picture of St. Francis of Assisi over the mantlepiece.

"Mrs. Bachman," the bishop began, "I have looked forward to this visit with you. Father Hespelein has told me encouraging things about the work you are doing among the poor."

Mrs. Bachman thanked His Lordship for his gracious words. "And how did you enjoy your visit to the Holy Father in Rome?" What she hesitated to ask was whether he had received their letter asking for approval.

"Wonderful, just wonderful. I must come back another time to tell you all about it. You did receive my answer from Rome?"

Mrs. Bachman was happy to know that the Bishop had received their letter, though his answer had not yet arrived. Bishop Neumann was sorry.

"Mrs. Bachman, at my audience with the Holy Father, he said a most extraordinary thing to me. He asked me to found an American branch of the Third Order of St. Francis here in Philadelphia to take care of the proposed orphanage. I must admit I was dumbfounded, almost despairing until I received your letter shortly afterwards. Mrs. Bachman, the ways of God are wonderful!"

Tears of joy glistened in Mrs. Bachman's eyes. Barbara and Anna Dorn knelt to kiss the bishop's ring. The girls were lined up on the staircase.

"Yes, Mrs. Bachman, we shall have a new branch of the Third Order of St. Francis here in Philadelphia. And you shall be the first Mother General."

This news was just too much. Mrs. Bachman had to sit down. Now she could consecrate her life to God as a nun. Barbara and Anna shook Father Hespelein's hand.

"Thanks be to our loving God. And thank you, Your Excellency," was all she could say.

"So, Mother," Bishop Neumann paused to let the word sink in. "So, Mother, Father Hespelein and I have arranged to hold the clothing ceremony after Vespers on Easter Monday in St. Peter's Church. At that time your year's novitiate will begin. Father Hespelein shall be your immediate superior, and I shall come over every week for a conference on religious life and other matters."

One year later in May, 1856, in the Bishop's private chapel, Mother Mary Francis Bachman, Sister Mary Margaret Ball and Sister Mary Bernardine Dorn vowed their lives to God at the hands of Bishop John Neumann and received from him their first Rule of Life.

Today the Franciscan Sisters now numbering 1,500 do glorious work for God in hospitals, orphanages and schools throughout the United States.

Bishop Neumann Blesses
Mother Francis O.S.F and
The Children
of St. Alphonsus
School
C. J. SHARKEY 59

EPISODE 19

Back Home in Bohemia

The whole town was buzzing with the news. A home-town boy, John Neumann, was coming home as a great bishop, the Bishop of Philadelphia in America. Civic pride called for an adequate welcome, a grand celebration befitting the occasion.

A Reception Committee was appointed to make plans for the music, the speeches and the decorations. But when would Bishop Neumann arrive? That was most important—the time of his arrival. Old Philip Neumann's letter from his son merely stated that the Bishop would visit his father on his way back from Rome. But what day, what hour? Without exact timing there could be no public welcome.

Bishop Neumann had arrived in Budweis in January, 1855, without prior announcement and stayed with the Bishop as his guest. That morning he and Bishop Jirisik lingered over their coffee cups.

"I must thank you for your gracious hospitality, Your Excellency," said Bishop Neumann. "You have been most kind. Now I must be leaving you."

"But why, Bishop, so suddenly?" Bishop Jirisik set his coffee cup down. "You said nothing of this before."

Bishop Neumann apologized. "I know Your Excellency will pardon me when I tell you that I am trying to keep the time of my departure a secret. If I know my people, they will be planning a big reception. This I must avoid at all costs."

Bishop Jirisik smiled. To what lengths some people will go merely to avoid publicity. "At least, Bishop Neumann, you must accept the loan of my personal sleigh and coachman to get you to Prachatitz."

A picture of the episcopal sleigh flashed before his mind: a bright green lacquered sleigh with the episcopal coat of arms emblazoned on the side and a coachman sitting on top.

"Thank you just the same. My nephew has just left for the livery to hire a sleigh. He should be back soon."

With sleigh bells ringing in broken rhythm, Bishop Neumann glided out through the suburbs of Budweis. The horse sniffing the clean crisp air from the hills settled to a slow trot. Bishop Neumann opened the curtains and sat back to chat with his nephew, John Berger. It was just wonderful to be coming back home after all those years in America, the burdens and the worries of his office lifted from his mind. He could imagine the surprise of his father as he saw his son come in the front door of the old homestead.

Snow covered the landscape for miles ahead—the hills, the farms and the old familiar road. Many a time he had walked this road to and from Budweis in his student days. Nineteen years ago almost to this very day he had left home and family and walked this same road to Budweis, a lonesome, homesick seminarian, not knowing whether he would be ordained or accepted by an American bishop. Now he was driving home in style in the fullness of the priesthood. And no one knew that he and his nephew were coming.

But why was the sleigh stopping? He looked out the window and saw a group of farmers kneeling in the snow and asking for his blessing. How did these people know he was coming? No matter now. He opened the window, leaned out, and gave them a big triple blessing. Further on, another halt and another group called for the bishop's blessing. Again he gave his blessing with a hearty greeting. The driver at Bishop Neumann's behest detached the sleigh bells from the harness. Still another group waited at the roadside for his arrival. Had his nephew let out the secret? No, John Berger had told no one except the owner of the livery stable.

What Bishop Neumann did not know was that the committee had found a young lad from Prachatitz, then a student at the Budweis Gymnasium, to watch out for Bishop Neumann's arrival in Budweis. By shrewd questions and using his own observation the lad learned that Bishop Neumann was staying at the Episcopal Residence. That morning, seeing his nephew leave the Residence, he followed him to the livery and listened. The rest was simply a matter of hiring a horse and riding ahead to spread the news.

As his sleigh approached the town of Nettolitz, he heard all the bells ringing and saw a crowd of people awaiting him. He alighted from the sleigh to greet them. Most of the older folks he knew, some were relatives of his dear departed mother. He had no choice but to stay that night with the pastor.

But he still must avoid the dreaded reception he knew awaited him the next day in Prachatitz.

The art of photography was in its infancy during John Neumann's lifetime, and only two portrait photographs were made of him, one in 1852 when he was consecrated, the other during a visit to his homeland in 1854. These have been models for the many paintings and statues since produced. This much-treasured original is in the Archives of the Redemptorist Fathers in Brooklyn, New York.

Archdiocese of Philadelphia

Talking it over with his nephew that night, it was decided that they would drive out of Nettolitz a mile or so, send the hired sleigh back to Budweis and walk the rest of the way. It was only a two hour walk and he knew a path that led into town by the rear.

Coming out of the parish house next morning with the pastor and his nephew, he found the street filled with people come to see him off. At the gate stood a splendid red lacquered sleigh with two spirited horses and two coachmen. Where was his own sleigh?

"There must be some mistake."

Bishop Neumann turned sharply to the pastor.

"No mistake, Your Excellency," the pastor assured him. "The Prince of Schwarzenberg has sent you his own sleigh with his personal compliments."

His little game was up. A smile curled the corners of his mouth. "May God forgive you, my good people," he addressed the crowd in the street. "Don't you realize that you are tempting an old bishop to thoughts of vanity?"

Vanity? Little Bishop Neumann? Everyone laughed and clapped and cheered as the red sleigh sped down the street and out of town.

A burst of cannon from the hilltops reverberated along the valley as the red sleigh came within sight of Prachatitz and all the bells rang out through the cold crisp air. Before the ancient city gates a big crowd awaited him with a brass band blaring out a lively march. His townspeople had outdone themselves. He could not let them down. Forgetful of his own preferences he yielded himself to the festive mood, listened to the speeches, graciously responding with a short heart-to-heart talk that captivated his listeners. An old atheist was heard to remark afterwards that if he listened much longer to the little Neumann boy he would be converted whether he wished to or not.

Coming out of the parish church after a Solemn *Te Deum* of gratitude to God, Bishop Neumann found the big red sleigh awaiting him.

He turned to the people. "You ask me to drive in state to my own father's house? Thank you, but I'll walk like I always did."

Old Philip Neumann was standing at the gate between his two daughters, Catherine and Louisa. Bishop Neumann hurried his steps. His old father, then over eighty years, dropped his cane, threw his arms around his boy and carried him up the steps into the house. Nineteen years after Ordination he gave his priestly blessing to his dear father and his sisters.

For one full week Bishop Neumann stayed in the old homestead, receiving all visitors, saying Mass each morning for his people and acceding to the many plans of the Reception Committee. But he was anxious to get back to Philadelphia.

Long before daylight, while the town was still asleep, Bishop Neumann in company with a priest friend glided over the snow and out through the gates of Prachatitz, refreshed and renewed for his many duties as Bishop of Philadelphia.

EPISODE 20

The Forty Hours

The idea grew gradually. On his pastoral visitation of the city parishes, Bishop Neumann noted with sorrow how few people took the time for a private visit to the Blessed Sacrament. What could he as the chief pastor of his people do to enliven their faith in the Real Presence? In memory he saw the Forty Hours Devotions in Europe with crowds coming all day to visit the Blessed Sacrament. Why not establish the Devotion here in Philadelphia, not in one or the other church, but throughout the whole diocese? To do this he needed the cooperation of his clergy.

One morning after settling some business with his Vicar General, Father Edward Sourin, Bishop Neumann told him of his plans for the Forty Hours. Father Sourin thought it a beautiful idea and urged him to carry it out. But Father Edmund Waldron, then in charge of trying to complete the building of the new cathedral, was absolutely against it, with no reasons given. Excellent priests, both of them, but gentle Father Sourin would be in favor of anything his bishop suggested, while Father Waldron—well, Father Waldron was a hard man to understand.

As head of the diocese, Bishop Neumann could on his own authority issue orders establishing the Forty Hours. But that was not John Neumann's way. Why not call a consultation with some of the outstanding priests of the diocese? That night before retiring he sent out invitations to seven of his priests asking them to meet with him at the Episcopal Residence on an important matter.

A cold December wind whisked the snow through the bare branches of the trees in front of the Episcopal Residence on Logan Square. In the big meeting room off the entrance hall, Bishop Neumann arranged the chairs around the long table while the cook built a wood fire in the big pot-bellied stove. Bishop Neumann was dressed as usual in his plain black Redemptorist habit.

"I know you won't mind my telling you, Bishop," said the cook, "but with all these priests coming, might it not be well to be dressed up more like a bishop?"

"You are right, Mary," Bishop Neumann was fond of his faithful cook and housekeeper. "Thank you. I should."

He went upstairs to make the change and shortly after, in response to the door bell, came down wearing the pectoral cross on the breast of his habit with the red zucchetto on his head.

It was Father Thaddeus Amat, the director of the diocesan seminary. Bishop Neumann welcomed him in, brushed the snow from his coat and hat, inquiring about his dear seminarians. By ten thirty when the last arrival was seated, Bishop Neumann took his place at the head of the table and opened the meeting with a prayer to the Holy Spirit.

"Gentlemen," he said in his low quiet voice, "I am grateful that you could come on a day like this. There is an important matter I would like very much to set before you. I need your advice and cooperation." As he presented and outlined his plan for the Forty Hours Devotion, his hearers sat back in amazement.

"So, Fathers," he concluded, "I am asking you for your opinions, your frank opinions. Father Amat, have you any ideas on the matter?"

When Father Amat pushed back his chair to rise, Bishop Neumann motioned him to stay seated.

"Your Excellency," said Father Amat, "as you present the project, I feel fully convinced of the desirability of the Forty Hours. But to look at it practically, the people are not yet ready. As it is, we are struggling merely to keep the faith alive."

"Thank you, Father Amat." Bishop Neumann jotted down a few notes. "And you, Father Domenec. What is your opinion?" Father Michael Domenec was pastor of the Church in Germantown.

"I admire your zeal, Your Excellency, and would be all in favor of it except for the fact that bigotry is still a power to be feared. As you know I am trying to build a new church in Germantown, and each morning I look out the window in dread that the Know-Nothings have wrecked another part of the construction. Now if the Forty Hours were to be introduced, what is to prevent such men from entering our churches and doing sacrilege against the Blessed Sacrament?"

Bishop Neumann clutched the armrests of his chair. Desecration to his Lord on the altar! He shuddered at the thought.

"And, Your Excellency," added Father James Ryder, the Jesuit Provincial, "we must not forget that less than ten years ago, two of our Philadelphia churches were burned to the ground by these same men."

Bishop Neumann turned pale. In the silence the crackling of the fire in the stove sounded ominously real.

"Father Cotty," resumed Bishop Neumann, still hoping for a bit of positive advice from the holy, zealous Father Joseph Cotty.

"Bishop, I know that your motive is the highest, and I admire you for it. But we should remember that no other bishop in the United States has come forward with such a plan."

"And," broke in Father Edmund Waldron, addressing his remarks to the assembled priests, "if my opinion is worth anything, I would like to bring out the fact that Philadelphians are not Bohemians."

The remark was highly improper, unfair, and if Father Waldron expected support from his colleagues, he saw only shame and chagrin, shame at the gratuitous insult to their holy bishop. An angry wind rattled the shutters outside the windows.

Bishop Neumann rose and rested his hands on the edge of the table. "Thank you, Reverend Fathers. Thanks for your candid remarks. I appreciate your frankness. A bishop must have the advice and suggestions of his priests." He raised his eyes and smiled. "Now, gentlemen, may I ask you to do me the honor of staying for dinner. Mary tells me she is preparing something special."

A smile went round the table. For the past half hour an appetizing fragrance had been drifting in from the kitchen. While the priests exchanged bits of pastoral news, Bishop Neumann slipped back to the kitchen to check with the cook and to the dining room to fill the wine glasses at each place.

When the blessing had been given and all were seated sipping their wine, the cook wheeled in a big steaming pot on a low serving cart.

"Gentlemen," announced Bishop Neumann, "I hope you will forgive the informality. Mary says it's a pot of Irish lamb stew." A round of happy laughter greeted the remark. With sleeves rolled up Bishop Neumann proceeded to push the cart from place to place, ladling out to each one according to his preference, serving his priests with such evident delight that no one even thought of offering to take his place.

In placing his plateful before Father Waldron, he gave his arm a warm slow squeeze. Father Waldron turned and looked up into the face of his bishop and smiled, a humble grateful smile. The manners of their little bishop were so sincerely polite and his conversation so lively that those closest to him did not notice how little he actually ate.

For weeks after this meeting with his priests, the thought of the Forty Hours refused to leave him, intruding itself even during the time of prayer. And always would follow the dreadful thought of the Blessed Sacrament being desecrated. That bigotry was still alive he was only too well aware. At that very time his name was being reviled in the Philadelphia newspapers because of his firm stand against the rebellious trustees of Holy Trinity Church. All this he could overlook. But desecration of the Blessed Sacrament on the altar was an entirely different matter. This he could not and would not risk.

It was long after midnight. Bishop Neumann was still at his desk, working by the dim light of a candle. Letters were neatly lined across the back of the desk ready to be folded into envelopes and addressed; a letter to the Sacred Congregation of Rites in Rome, a

Bishop Neumann Advocate
of the Forty
Hours
Devotion
c Neumann Center, Philadelphia, Pa

letter to the Rector of St. Peter's Church, letters to the pastors in Lancaster County, notifying them of his coming visitation.

The light grew dimmer. Drawing the candlestick nearer he saw that the flame had burned down into the socket. From its flame he lit another candle stub and half asleep he set it not into the socket of the candlestick but on the back of his desk and suddenly collapsed in his chair, exhausted by the labors of a long hard day.

Not long after he awoke with a start. The room reeked of smoke, the candle was blazing in a pool of wax and his letters were burned and charred. He leaned forward to look closer. The letters were burned and charred but only around the edges and the writing was still intact. Thank God the whole room had not gone up in flames. He dropped to his knees. It was then he heard an inner voice as distinctly as if the words were spoken into his ear.

"Just as the writing was not consumed by the flames, so my Presence on the altar shall not be desecrated. So hesitate no longer to carry out your plan for My Greater Glory."

In April, 1853, at his first diocesan synod when all the pastors were assembled and the theologians, Bishop Neumann again presented his plan to inaugurate a schedule for the Forty Hours Devotion in the diocese. Though no mention was made of the charred letters or of the interior voice, his words carried such a warmth of conviction that his motion was passed by a surprising majority.

A decree was sent out in the Bishop's own handwriting to all the pastors, officially inaugurating the Forty Hours Devotion on a diocesan-wide basis.

St. Philip Neri Church was designated as the church where it would begin.

At the opening Mass on the Feast of Corpus Christi the church was crowded with people and for three days and two nights there was a constant stream of the faithful coming to adore the Blessed Sacrament enthroned on the high altar. And for three days the silent figure of their little bishop was seen in the side aisle rapt in prayer and happy communion with his Divine Master.

From St. Philip Neri's the Forty Hours progressed through the diocese, everywhere drawing crowds of people. God had blessed the efforts of His faithful bishop. Gradually other dioceses followed the trend until the Forty Hours Devotion became one of the highlights of American Catholicity.

EPISODE 21

With His Boots On

He had not been feeling well for some days. Though advised to see a doctor, Bishop Neumann felt that he could not spare the time from his duties.

At lunch that day he took nothing except a cup of hot tea. Father Carter and Bishop Wood, his coadjutor, alarmed at the pallor of his face, urged him to go to bed. With a disarming smile, he assured them that the bad feeling would wear off as it always did. They were not convinced.

To divert their attention he began to entertain them with reminiscences of his seminary days back home in Budweis, adding the story of the old farmer and his two guldens with such genuine delight that they both concluded he could not be too sick, little realizing that this was the last story they would hear from the lips of their brave little bishop.

Father Urban, his former subject in Baltimore, dropped in after lunch for a friendly visit and found Bishop Neumann working at his desk. His face looked unearthly pale.

"Bishop," he interrupted, "how are you feeling?"

Bishop Neumann turned in his chair but could not seem to focus his vision on his visitor.

"Don't you know me, Bishop?" Father Urban was frightened.

"Of course, of course, Father Urban. How could I forget those good old days together in St. Alphonsus'?" He gave Father Urban a hearty handshake.

"Bishop, you don't look at all well." Father Urban was not taken in by the sudden cheerfulness. "Your eyes? Your color?"

Bishop Neumann confessed that he had been feeling poorly for some days, that in fact he had a strange feeling he never had experienced before.

"But," he added, "I have to go out soon on some business, and the walk in the fresh air will do me good. It always does."

As Father Urban was leaving, the bishop quietly remarked, "Father, a man must always be prepared. Death comes when and where the good God wills it."

Father Urban knelt for the bishop's blessing on his parish mission in New York City and went downstairs, dismissing the remark as just another pious thought.

Neumann's business that afternoon was with the lawyer to sign settlement papers for a plot of land for another new parochial school. Though his signature, usually so precise, was very shaky, the lawyer thought nothing of it, because the Bishop seemed so happy about the transaction. From there he was to go to the express office to inquire about a consecrated chalice lost in transit to Father Kopf in Bellefontaine.

Walking west on Vine Street he had to go against a cold wind sweeping across the Schuykill River and to face the glare of the sun from a new fallen snow. The sidewalk was slippery. He was thankful that he had thought to put on his hobnail boots, the rough boots he used on pastoral visitation out in the counties.

But the walk in the fresh air instead of improving the bad feeling only made him worse. Often before he had worked off such spells. But this one? A sudden spasm convulsed his chest, a deep thrust of pain choked off his breathing. He leaned against a fence.

"O God," he panted, "this is for You. You know that." Perspiration gathered on his forehead. He waited until the pain receded and he could breathe more freely.

The attack left him so weak he decided to postpone the express office and get back home. He staggered along Vine Street from 12th to 13th Street. At the corner a dull pain shot through his head from temple to temple. He waited a moment.

"Dear Lord— if this— be death— take me, Lord— for my diocese."

A veil of haze blurred his vision. The jangling of sleigh bells and hoof beat of horses seemed to come from far away. Like a drunkard he staggered across the street through the traffic, mindless of angry drivers and swerving sleighs. He reached the other side safely and at the second house from the corner, his knees gave way and he slumped unconscious on the front door steps.

Several had seen him fall and ran to help him. The front door opened and a kindly voice called down: "Bring in the poor man." He opened the other half of the double door. "Bring him into the parlor."

Two young men lifted the frail little figure, carried him up the front stairs and laid him on the carpet near the warmth of an open fireplace. No one knew what to do for a dying man. Someone lifted his head and placed a cushion underneath. The light from the blazing logs threw shadows on his shrivelled features. But who was he? In his pockets they found

Death
in the
Master's
service
c Neumann Center, Philadelphia, Pa.

some small change, the receipt for Father Kopf's chalice and an old worn rosary. On opening his coat they found the pectoral cross, the insignia of a Catholic Bishop. A messenger was sent to the Episcopal residence on Logan Square.

His breathing grew slower till with one gentle gasp, John Neumann breathed out his soul into the hands of his Maker, into the presence of the loving God for whom he had worked and spent his life. It was three o'clock in the afternoon of January 5, 1860.

Father Carter arrived on the scene with the Holy Oils. One look told him his bishop was gone. John Neumann had died at the age of forty-nine, prematurely worn out by his unstinting labors in the service of his heavenly King.

Bishop Neumann was dead. The news of his sudden death spread throughout the city, passed on by word of mouth from door to door, from one street to the next, to Protestants and Catholics alike. By nightfall a hush of stunned grief hung like a pall over the city of Philadelphia. Bishop Neumann was no more.

The telegraph wires flashed the news to the remote corners of his vast diocese. Hardened coal miners, burly farmers, mill workers, the poor and the down-trodden who had known and loved the itinerant bishop who travelled their roads with the Mass kit on his back—everyone grieved as for the loss of a personal friend. They would never see him again. Bishop Neumann was no more.

At the funeral procession from Logan Square to St. John's Pro-cathedral on Thirteenth and Chestnut Streets, officials of Philadelphia admitted that never before had the city seen a greater demonstration of public sorrow. Along the line of march from door-steps and windows, from sidewalks and roof tops thousands

gazed in mute sorrow as the procession passed with the plain wooden casket in the glass-walled hearse. Bishop Neumann was no more.

Since during his lifetime Bishop Neumann had expressed the wish to be buried among his Redemptorist confreres, Archbishop Francis Kenrick directed the sacred remains be brought to St. Peter's Church at Fifth and Girard Avenue. All that day and into the night crowds filed up the center aisle to have one last look at their friend and bishop and to touch rosaries and handkerchiefs to the remains of him whom they considered already a saint. They came in unending numbers—the poor he had helped in their need, the sinners he had brought back to the Sacraments, the nuns he had directed in the path of holiness, the old, the sick and the lame, and the children he had loved so well during his life among them.

Older priests, men inured to the woes and sorrows of life, were not ashamed to let the tears fall as their bishop's mortal remains were let down in the tomb at St. Peter's. The Philadelphia priesthood had lost its model of a perfect priest.

To that tomb beneath a marble slab in the sanctuary floor they came the next day and the next day and continued to come. People who had known and loved him in life, people who grew to know him after his departure knelt at his tomb to ask his help. Many favors and graces were obtained through his intercession. A blind girl on the last day of her novena to Bishop Neumann received her eyesight. The crowds increased to such a surprising degree that Archbishop Patrick Ryan in 1886 petitioned Rome that Bishop Neumann's cause be introduced.

The short, unknown seminarian who had left home and country to come to America and work for souls was now on the high road to sainthood.

EPISODE 22

John Neumann in Glory

The Beatification of Bishop Neumann was scheduled for October 13, 1963. The Second Vatican Council, then in session at St. Peter's in Rome, had been recessed for the occasion.

That bright sunny morning thirty thousand pilgrims began streaming through the doors of the great basilica. Visitors from all over Europe and from the United States took their places inside the vast edifice or found standing room in the aisles. From windows high up near the ceiling a soft light filtered down on the assemblage in the Chapel of the Chair. Situated almost beneath the mighty dome of Michelangelo and in the rear of the magnificent baldachino of the main altar, the "Chapel" is in itself more like a cathedral.

A gasp of suppressed excitement passed through the crowd when the bishops in rippling purple and the cardinals in flaming red passed up the center and took their places in the double rows of chairs facing each other.

Promptly at ten o'clock a procession of prelates emerged from the sacristy and stood in a circle around the altar. A document, the official document of Beatification signed by His Holiness, Pope Paul VI, was handed by Cardinal Larraona to Cardinal Marella, the arch-priest of St. Peter's Basilica, who in turn passed it on to one of his canons to be read. A hush gripped the crowd. This was the moment for which so many had prayed and waited.

In loud clear tones that echoed through the vastness the decree was read, proclaiming Bishop John Nepomucene Neumann, C.SS.R., as a duly approved Blessed of the Holy Roman Catholic Church.

"Te Deum laudamus," the voice of Cardinal Krol of Philadelphia sang out loud and clear. The great organ of St. Peter's and the Sistine Choir took up the anthem and at that moment the Chapel, the whole basilica burst into a dazzling brilliance. There high above the altar in Bernini's golden "Window of Glory" was revealed the painting of little Bishop Neumann in flowing purple mantle ascending on a cloud of angels, on his face a look of heavenly rapture as he beholds the beautiful vision of the loving God he had so faithfully served.

"Thee the whole world proclaims our eternal God," continued the Sistine Choir from somewhere high up behind the arches.

"To Thee the Apostles and the Prophets and the white-robed martyrs sing out in praise." The thirty thousand, recovered from the first thrill of joy, joined their voices to that of the Sistine Choir.

"To Thee the Angels and the Powers of heaven, the Cherubim and the Seraphim cry out in unending song—Holy, Holy, Holy."

Cardinals and bishops, Redemptorists in their plain black habits, beribboned diplomats in the draped balcony, the whole concourse of people, even the reporters and camera men joined in one grand outpouring of praise and thanksgiving.

The house at 1218 Vine was demolished when the Street was widened for a traffic throughway. At that time, the fireplace before which the Bishop died was removed and preserved. Together with a portrait of "The Little Bishop," it now occupies a place of honor in "The Neumann Room" on the top floor of the Archdiocesan office building in Philadelphia. The stone front step on which the Bishop collapsed is retained at the Neumann shrine.

Archdiocese of Philadelphia

"To Thee the entire Church on earth returns thanks," thanksgiving to God who today has given us another blessed, Bishop John Nepomucene Neumann, now among the Saints in heaven.

Prayer in honor of John Neumann:

"O God, who willed that John, Your confessor and bishop, should excel by his priestly ministrations, grant in Your goodness that following his words and example we too may arrive at eternal glory. Amen."

Memorable Dates in the Life of John Neumann

Mar. 28, 1811	Born in Prachatitz, Bohemia
Nov. 1, 1823	Entered High School in Budweis
Nov. 1, 1831	Entered the Seminary of Budweis
Oct. 8, 1833	Transferred to the Seminary of Prague
July 2, 1835	Left Prague ready for ordination
Apr. 20, 1836	Sailed from France hoping to be ordained in New York
June 2, 1836	Arrived in New York City
June 25, 1836	Ordained by Bishop John Dubois in old St. Patrick's Cathedral on Mott Street
July 12, 1836	Began his work for souls on the Niagara frontier
Oct. 18, 1840	Welcomed into the Congregation of the Most Holy Redeemer

Jan. 16, 1842	Pronounced his perpetual vows in St. James Church in Baltimore
Mar. 1844	Appointed Superior of St. Philomena's in Pittsburgh
Mar. 15, 1847	Appointed Vice-Provincial of the Redemptorists in the United States
Aug. 1847	Helped to establish the School Sisters of Notre Dame in Baltimore
Feb. 10, 1848	Sworn in as a naturalized citizen of the U.S.
Mar. 28, 1852	Consecrated Bishop of Philadelphia by Archbishop Francis P. Kenrick in St. Alphonsus Church in Baltimore
May 3, 1852	Organized the first parochial school system in the United States
Apr. 1853	Established the Forty Hours Devotion in his diocese, the first such in America
Dec. 8, 1854	Present in St. Peter's in Rome for the proclama- of the Dogma of Mary's Immaculate Conception
Feb. 1855	Visited his old father in Prachatitz
May 1855	Organized a new order of the Sisters of St. Francis
Apr. 26, 1857	Given an assistant in the person of Bishop James Wood
Jan. 5, 1860	Collapsed in the street and died in the home of a stranger
Dec. 11, 1921	Declared Venerable by Pope Benedict XV
Oct. 13, 1963	Declared Blessed by Pope Paul VI
June 19, 1977	Canonization

ADDITIONAL LIVES OF SAINTS AVAILABLE:

Every Man's Challenge

Daughters of St. Paul

Brief lives of 38 saints—factual and realistic. This volume responds to the ever-present desire for "true-life" profiles that inspire.

346 pages; deluxe $7.00; cloth $5.00

Families That Followed the Lord

Martin P. Harney, SJ

This book contains the lives of over one hundred fifty brother and sister saints of various nationalities, places, and times. This account of fraternal and religious loyalty, which blends the best of what is human and divine, cannot fail to touch and inspire the reader of today.

145 pages; cloth $3.95; paper $2.95

Hands for Others

Sister Louise Passero, FMA

Mary Mazzarello, a peasant woman of our times, though handicapped by poverty and little learning, founds a religious congregation, the Salesians, dedicated to teaching, nursing and social works of the Church. A compelling biography of a woman of great hope.

80 pages; Magister paperback 50c

Heavenly Friends, A Saint for Each Day

Rosalie Marie Levy

A superb book, epitomizing the lives of more than 400 famous saints.

486 pages; deluxe $7.00; cloth or plastic $5.00; paper $4.00

Joseph, the Just Man

Rosalie Marie Levy

A complete biography, supplemented with accounts of favors granted and selections of special prayers.

285 pages; cloth $4.00; paper $3.00

Joseph: The Man Closest to Jesus

Francis L. Filas, SJ

Never before has all this wealth of intensely interesting and little-known facts about St. Joseph been compiled into a single book. This can truly be called a "little Summa" of St. Joseph, as the only survey existing in any language of the complete life, theology, and devotional history of St. Joseph.

682 pages; cloth $6.50; paper $5.50

The Legacy of St. Patrick

Martin P. Harney, SJ

The legacy of St. Patrick, which he would bequeath to his brethren and their descendants, was his own holy idealism. It can be found in his two writings, the Confession of St. Patrick and the Letters to the Soldiers of Coroticus.

A thoughtful perusal of the Confession and of the Letter will reward the reader with a true and an intimate knowledge of St. Patrick.

148 pages; cloth $3.00

Magnificent Witnesses

Martin P. Harney, SJ

Simple, heart-warming, soul-stirring sketches of the English and Welsh martyrs, canonized by Pope Paul VI on October 25, 1970. The martyrs included 13 secular priests, 20 religious (of 5 orders), 4 laymen and 3 laywomen. All gave their lives for the fundamental doctrine of the Primacy of the Pope.

80 pages; cloth $2.00

St. Gemma, the Passion Flower

Msgr. Joseph Bardi

A touching biography, the memory of which will be a source of consolation in time of suffering.

182 pages; cloth $2.00

St. Joan of Arc, Virgin—Soldier

Msgr. Leon Cristiani

The author scrupulously strives to present the simple, naked, historical truth about the life and times of Joan of Arc. He also outlines the supernatural in Joan's life in all its clarity.

160 pages; cloth $4.00; paper $3.00

St. Martin de Porres

Richard Cardinal Cushing

For forty-five years St. Martin dedicated himself almost entirely to the performance of spiritual and corporal works of mercy. "A thumbnail sketch in which the 'digitus Dei' clearly appears in the life and work of St. Martin."
"Central California Register"

80 pages; cloth $1.50

Mother Seton—wife, mother, educator, foundress, saint

Daughters of St. Paul

This fast-paced life of "an authentic daughter of America" (Pope John's term) is completed by selections from Mother Seton's own writings —Spiritual Gems—that permit us to glimpse the deep spirituality of the first American-born saint.

140 pages; cloth $3.95; paper $2.95

Saint of the Impossible

Daughters of St. Paul

Fast-paced chapters tell of St. Rita's childhood and youth, of her will to succeed in her stormy marriage, of the transformation worked in her husband by her prayer and suffering for him, of her two sons, their death and her widowed loneliness. Even St. Rita's desire for religious life was thwarted at first, but the belief in God's unfailing care never left her... and she succeeded.

104 pages; cloth $3.95

St. Paul, Apostle and Martyr

Igino Giordani

St. Paul inspires many a modern-day laborer, housewife, intellectual, businessman, politician and statesman to bring God's kingdom to all. "What the author desired—the presentation of a living, human Paul—he admirably achieved." "Catholic Book Reporter"

38 full-color illustrations and 33 in black and white.

392 pages; deluxe $9.00; cloth $7.00; paper $6.00

St. Teresa of Avila

Giorgio Papasogli

It took the author a year's visit to Spain, exhaustive research and an intensive study of all the existing material before he was ready to write. The result was an entirely new biography of one of the most written-about women in the world.

410 pages; cloth $5.00

St. Theresa, the Little Flower

Sister Gesualda of the Holy Spirit

The heart-warming story of a modern saint known and venerated the world over!

270 pages; cloth $4.00; paper $3.00

Three Ways of Love

Frances Parkinson Keyes

The world-famous author here captures the romance, the tragedy and the history of three great women: St. Agnes, whose name has become synonymous with courage; St. Frances of Rome, a mother and the protectress of the poor and sick; and St. Catherine of Siena, the famous ambassadress and stateswoman.

304 pages; cloth $6.00; paper $5.00

Please order from addresses on following page.

Sisters,
Please send me:

____

____

____

____

name ______________________________

address ______________________________

city ________________ state __________ zip ________

Enclosed is my payment for $________________

Daughters of St. Paul

IN MASSACHUSETTS
50 St. Paul's Avenue, Boston, Ma. 02130
172 Tremont Street, Boston, Ma. 02111
IN NEW YORK
78 Fort Place, Staten Island, N.Y. 10301
59 East 43rd St., New York, N.Y. 10017
625 East 187th Street, Bronx, N.Y. 10458
525 Main Street, Buffalo, N.Y. 14203
IN NEW JERSEY
84 Washington Street, Bloomfield, N.J. 07003
IN CONNECTICUT
202 Fairfield Avenue, Bridgeport, Ct. 06603
IN OHIO
2105 Ontario St. (at Prospect Ave.), Cleveland, Oh. 44115
25 E. Eighth Street, Cincinnati, Oh. 45202
IN PENNSYLVANIA
1719 Chestnut St., Philadelphia, Pa. 19103
IN FLORIDA
2700 Biscayne Blvd., Miami, Fl. 33137
IN LOUISIANA
4403 Veterans Memorial Blvd.,
Metairie, La. 70002
86 Bolton Avenue, Alexandria, La. 71301
IN MISSOURI
1001 Pine St. (at North 10th), St. Louis, Mo. 63101
IN TEXAS
114 East Main Plaza, San Antonio, Tx. 78205
IN CALIFORNIA
1570 Fifth Avenue, San Diego, Ca. 92101
278 17th Street, Oakland, Ca. 94612
46 Geary Street, San Francisco, Ca. 94108
IN HAWAII
1184 Bishop St., Honolulu, Hi. 96813
IN ALASKA
750 West 5th Avenue
Anchorage, Ak. 99501
IN CANADA
3022 Dufferin Street, Toronto 395, Ontario, Canada
IN ENGLAND
57, Kensington Church Street, London W. 8, England
IN AUSTRALIA
58, Abbotsford Rd., Homebush, N.S.W., Sydney 2140,
Australia